WOES OF APPALACHIAN WOMEN

WARRIORS AND SURVIVORS

AUDRINE WILSON TUCKER

Wasteland Press
www.wastelandpress.net
Shelbyville, KY USA

Woes of Appalachian Women:
Warriors and Survivors
by Audrine Wilson Tucker

First Printing – March 2021
Paperback ISBN: 978-1-68111-399-9

Printed in the U.S.A.

0   1   2

TABLE OF CONTENTS

FOREWORD 1

Cora Allen 3

Abbie Allen... 5

The Cigarette... 9

Cora Allen's School.. 13

Cora Allen and Joey Johnson 17

June Allen 21

The Abusive Husband 24

Bossy and Fido 30

Shirley Parmley 37

The Joy Ride 43

The Drunks... 45

Ruthie Allen 49

Hester and Harley... 54

The Death 56

The Baby 58

The Old Crow Man... 64

Pastor Pascal 73

Nancy Maggard and the Veteran 77

The Rape 88

The Prisoner and the Taxi Driver 93

The Miner and Bootlegger 99

The Haunted Barn 104

Amy Johnson 110

The Strangers 119

FOREWORD

These stories are based on true events. The names and places have been changed in order to protect the identities of those described. Most of these individuals if they are still living are in their late 70's or 80's. The following stories took place in the early to mid-20th century. They depict real life at the time for many families and aspects of the stories herein were common for the time and place. There were numerous tragedies and untimely deaths due to poor medical conditions, drinking, accidents, or negligence on the part of those in power. The poor roads combined with common alcoholism often lead to the untimely deaths of both the drunk driver and any unlucky passersby.

To make matters worse, this time period marked the final decline of the coal mining industry in this part of Appalachia. Communities that had been built for and thrived under the leadership of coal mining companies were now cut off from their lifelines and were dying. There was a mass exodus of able bodied young people to major cities looking for jobs in the newly burgeoning industrial sector. Many of these workers had difficulty adjusting to city life and longed for the mountains.

Because of this, it was common to come home every weekend and stay with family. These were large families; when a spouse died often the children were parceled out to relatives or orphans homes. In many cases these children were mistreated.

A number of young women sought security in times of poverty by marrying older men with some kind of pension or government benefits. This often meant that husbands would die and leave their relatively younger wives with children to support, and often this caused the cycle to continue. Some people were influenced greatly by the church, but others were not. Because of this, there were men who did not have any scruples about treating their wives and children with cruelty instead of love or understanding.

This book reveals the seamy side of Appalachian life that was prevalent during this time of poverty. It's easy to gloss over this time and place with a rose-colored and historically inaccurate picture of traditional families getting by happily through hard work and faith alone. The truth is that help comes as often as not from unexpected places, even total strangers. And this unique aspect of Appalachian life was in many cases the saving grace of the young women depicted in this book.

In the following pages you will find multiple stories featuring different traumatic aspects of Appalachian women's lives as well as tales that will help put you in the mind of what the world was like in general. In order to represent the way a mountain person would tell a story these pieces have been interspersed throughout the core storyline which follows the life of Cora Allen. In other words, along the way we will be "chasing rabbits".

Cora Allen

Cora Allen was the youngest of eleven children born to Bertha and Charles Allen. She lived in the Appalachian area of Kentucky. Bertha stuttered and was slightly mentally challenged. She was an abusive mother and had various strict ideas about parenting. Once she told a child something, she never changed her mind regardless of their pleading. Charles was very controlling and abusive too. He delighted in finding weaknesses in a person and capitalizing on them. If he came home and anything or any person upset him, he beat the first person that he met, sometimes even his wife.

Charles mocked Bertha's stuttering often. He was about twenty years older than seventeen-year-old Bertha when they married. His first wife and two children had died from the flu. He still had four children from his first marriage that Bertha helped raise. Bertha's mother had begged her not to marry Charles because she knew he was a mean man. Since there was no birth control, he and Bertha had a house full of children. By the time Cora was born, most of her siblings had already married and had homes of their own. Because her older sisters wanted to escape their home lives, each of them was pregnant before their marriage. Needless to say, Cora did not have a nurturing family.

Abbie Allen

Abbie, Cora's sister, had a horrible home life. Abbie Allen had a horrible home life. Her parents, Bertha and Charles, were cruel people. Charles beat Bertha often, as well as his eight daughters and three sons. If anyone or anything displeased him he flew into a rage and beat the offender or the closest one he met.

Charles Allen drew Social Security from having worked in the mines as well as welfare checks each month. Although he was a hard worker as a young man, the years and the damage he sustained to his health from his time as a miner had turned him into a bitter and dejected person who was uninterested in working, kindness, or being a decent father.

He watched for weakness and what he considered disobedience in any of his children or wife. He was happiest when he was "correcting" his wife and children.

Abbie was a hard worker from the time she could do chores and for the rest of her life. When she reached her teens, she washed clothes for families on a washboard for $1.00 a day. Often she had to carry water from the creek to heat and wash each load of the families' clothes. Then she hung them on the line to dry. Sometimes she even had to iron the clothes. Abbie went back to the creek and got more water and heated it to continue washing the rest of the clothes.

Charles got mad at Abbie one afternoon and beat her. That's when she started saving her money for the big plan she was organizing in her mind. At fourteen, she planned to leave home and take a bus to Indiana where she had family members that would help her. She wrote a letter to her sister Lois letting her know which day she would come, and when the bus would arrive. She washed her hair and bathed. When her hair dried she rolled up her side hair in French rolls and tied her hair in a ponytail. She packed some of her better clothes in a shopping bag, put on a white blouse with a green skirt and brown Poll Parrot shoes. Then she walked to the bus station and bought a ticket to Indiana. Upon arriving, she called Lois, to come pick her up.

Lois drove down to the station and got Abbie, and took her home with her. Abbie babysat Lois's three children aged six, eight, and ten. Lois went back to work to earn enough money to get a new car and pay Abbie an allowance for her help. Lois's husband stayed some other place most of the time, but he did provide for the family.

The children changed clothes often each day and the laundry piled up. Abbie told Lois that she would only wash once or twice a week, so Lois made the children stop changing clothes so much.

Lois's house had a cistern with a pitcher pump in the kitchen and an outside drain. The family drank and bathed in water from the cistern and had rain barrels under the house's drain spouts which they used for washing their clothes. They had an outside toilet and a potty-chair inside to use at night. They emptied the pot each morning, washed it, and left it outside to air until that night.

Lois's house also had a bathtub with an outside drain. They had to heat the bath water in pans on the stove to pour into the bathtub.

Abbie's mother cried many times while Abbie was gone. Although it may seem strange, despite the fact that Bertha was consistently cruel to Abbie, once she was gone she missed her greatly. Every time Bertha felt she couldn't stand her absence anymore, she would pen a letter begging Abbie to come home. Abbie would answer each of the letters the same way: she enjoyed her new life and would not return to her old one for anything.

Abbie married an older man, Eddie Clayborn when she was sixteen. He loved her and treated her well. He also provided well for her according to the time.

Soon she got pregnant. Abbie wanted to go home to have her baby. Because they would need several days before and after the birth itself, Eddie couldn't take off work to go with her. Being gone so long would jeopardize his job. Seventeen-year-old Abbie decided to go alone on a bus. She went to her parents' home and waited for the baby's birth.

A few days later she went into labor. The family called a midwife to help with the delivery. The men and younger children slept in the barn loft the night of the delivery. Abbie stayed at home until her baby boy, Edward, was two weeks old. Then she bought a bus ticket and she and the baby went back to Indiana to Eddie. They were very happy and had a good life.

* * * *

Cora managed to survive her younger years. One of her siblings got the mumps and brought them home to her. She became very ill, and her health was damaged. Afterwards she had terrible migraines that made her sick at her stomach, and she could barely walk. As Cora got older her parents didn't send her to school.

One of her brothers got some primer books from the county board of education, and gradually taught her to read, count and do some arithmetic. Later she learned the multiplication tables.

The truancy officer came to the Allens' home to find out why Cora wasn't in school.

Bertha answered, "Just look at her, look at how she walks. And she gets bad sick headaches almost every day. How can she learn if she is sick all the time and can't walk?"

The officer replied, "Either send her, or your check will be reduced or cut off."

Bertha became very angry because her family depended on Cora's disability check. They got a fifteen-dollar welfare check and a Social Security check each month. They had to enroll her in school and placed ten-year-old Cora in the primer with the little kids. Her mother made her wear stockings and a dress that almost reached her ankles. She also platted Cora's long hair. Cora was embarrassed to be ten and in the primer, and by the way her mother dressed her so differently from the other girls.

The Cigarette

Discipline was sometimes very harsh in the schools of the poor parts of Appalachia. The financial connection with truancy and government benefits only served to increase the tension between parents, students and teachers.

Once a retired sheriff's deputy and widower named Mark Jones married a widow named Maggie Harper. Between them they had seven children. Maggie had three boys and a fourteen-year-old girl named Bonnie. Mark had two boys and a fourteen-year-old girl named Jenny.

As the children walked home from school one afternoon, the girls stopped at a neighbor's house for a few minutes before going home to do their chores. There was a sixteen-year-old boy sitting on the couch smoking. Bonnie took the cigarette out of his hand and took a puff, and then she handed it to Jenny who took a puff too before handing it back to the boy on the couch.

The next day at school one of the neighbors' small children told the principal Mr. Ashley that the girls were smoking. He called them into the office and questioned them.

He asked, "Were you girls smoking yesterday on the way home?"

The girls answered in unison, "No!"

He answered, "You're lying. I was told that you were smoking!"

Bonnie said, "We don't smoke! You can ask anyone!"

He said, "Stop sassing me, you will have to take your punishment for smoking, lying, and sassing."

He whipped Jenny first. He had her bend over his desk and hit her four times, hard. Next he whipped Bonnie six licks. It hurt very badly. They were in pain and embarrassed for the rest of the day.

When they got home their parents saw them and realized something was wrong. Upon examining their backsides, they saw dark bruises on them. The parents were very angry. The next day they went to the doctor and let them witness the bruises. They took pictures of the girls' rear ends.

They consulted a lawyer to file a lawsuit against Mr. Ashley. He said, "Do you know any other parents whose kids have been beaten? If you can get them to go to court with you, we can get his license suspended."

Mark and Maggie had heard of two boys that had been beaten, too. Upon questioning them and the boys' parents, one parent pointed to his rifle and said, "If it happens anymore I will take care of it myself, but I won't go to court."

The other parents said, "If it happens again, I'll catch him out some night and beat him up, but I won't go to court."

The next day Bonnie went to Indiana on a bus. She babysat and did housework for her sister. At the age of sixteen, the sister signed for her to marry an eighteen-year-old boy she had met there. Although they were young, they made a good life together.

Jenny didn't go back to school. Principal Ashley sent word for her to come back, or part of the checks the family drew would be cut. Jenny was determined not to go to that school. She got a pillow and tied it around her waist up under her dress and pretended to be pregnant. She wore it all her waking hours every day. All her friends thought she was really pregnant. The truancy officer made a few visits to their home. Jenny told them she was pregnant and wasn't allowed to attend school. The retired deputy's check went from thirty dollars a month to fifteen. The other check he drew could not be harmed.

When school started the next fall, Jenny took the seventh grade over at a different school. She lied and told everyone that she had moved to a house in another community but it was just an empty house. She still lived at home. For the eighth grade, Jenny moved in with an aunt and uncle, and continued attending the second school.

After she graduated high school she moved to Chicago, and lived with her married sister until she got married herself. Years later she died from leukemia.

* * * *

The county supervisor came out and checked on Cora's grasp of the basics of education. After this interrogation, the supervisor moved Cora up to the second grade. Later she was moved up to fourth grade when they learned that she knew her multiplication tables.

Cora was not happy at school because the kids made fun of her. They also made fun of what she brought for lunch. She had a quart Clabber Girl baking powder can with milk and cornbread in it. Bertha had made a drawstring pouch for the baking powder can. Cora let it dangle down from her wrist by the strings when she carried it. The other kids had gallon syrup buckets with biscuits, eggs, or sausage. Some of the more prosperous families had "light bread" sandwiches.

One time the teacher brought a used wine corduroy coat to school for the coatless Cora. She gave it to Cora in front of the other students. Cora was embarrassed and just left it lying on her desk at the end of the day.

The teacher said, "Cora, here's your coat. It's cold outside; take it with you."

Cora answered, "I don't want it. You embarrassed me by letting the other kids know that you gave it to me."

The teacher said, "What does it matter? You need a coat!"

Cora cried, "Give it to someone else; I don't want it."

Conditions at Cora's school were very primitive anyway. In cold weather, it could be particularly harsh.

Cora Allen's School

The Allen family attended a one-room school in Eastern Kentucky in the 40's and 50's. The building was covered in white weatherboard. It had windows on the sides, a door at the back, and a blackboard across the front. There was a large potbelly stove in the center of the room that was used for heating in the winter. A small wooden table at one side of the room held two water buckets with a dipper. There were two shelves over the buckets that held individual drinking cups. On each side of the door, nails were partly driven into the wall at an upward angle to hold coats and toboggans. Different-sized wooden and metal school desks were stationed in neat rows, and a teacher's desk and chair were placed at the front of the room.

It was winter and very cold. That year Bertha Allen had bought Cora and Ella coats for twenty five cents each at a used clothing store. They were so long that they almost came down to their ankles, but they kept the girls toasty warm. Every year the county board of education furnished coal for the stoves, but this year it hadn't been delivered yet. It would probably be two or three weeks before it would arrive. When the girls got to school, a large boy named Lincoln had unlocked the door, but there wasn't any heat.

He said, "The coal house is empty and I'm waiting for another boy to get here so we can chop wood off the hillside for a fire."

Cora said, "They might not be here at all, or they might wait to see smoke come from the chimney before they come. We can't wait on them. We need heat and Mrs. Johnson doesn't want us bumming coal from a neighbor. Let me and Ella take coal buckets out to the railroad tracks and collect some coal that has fallen from the train cars."

Lincoln said, "Let me get these two buckets as well, so we can get four buckets and heat the schoolhouse all day."

The children soon collected enough coal to fill the buckets and headed back to school.

Cora said, "Lincoln, you take out the ashes and sweep around the stove while Ella and I go out on the hillside to collect kindling."

Lincoln said, "Okay, but hurry. I'm COLD!"

The girls rushed out to the hillside and found a fallen dead tree. They broke off a lot of different sized limbs and brought them back to the schoolhouse. Lincoln put some paper and small twigs in the stove. Later he added some large limbs and a few pieces of coal. He used a cigarette lighter to get the paper burning. After the fire was burning well, he dumped one whole bucket of coal into the stove and soon the stove's belly became red hot.

Cora said, "Lincoln, you better be careful how much coal you put in it, because you might burn the house down, especially if it's been treated for smelting."

The girls poured water out of the buckets into a wash pan and placed it on the stove to heat. Then all three children used soap and washed the coal dust off of their hands and let them dry from the heat of the stove. The girls got brooms and swept the whole room while Lincoln carried in fresh buckets of water. When the other children saw the smoke coming out of the chimney, they left home and trooped into the school.

One big girl, named Mary, rang the school bell 'for books'. When the bell rang, it signaled the children to take their seats and get ready for class. Everyone sat down and started their morning devotions. They sang "Good Morning to You", "Dixie" and "America". Then, Mary read from the Bible.

About that time, Mrs. Johnson came in the door. In other words, she had ridden a bus out to the school. Since she was a teacher, the bus company let her ride for free. She took off her coat, and placed her belongings on her desk.

"Good morning, I see they brought out the coal and you all have a fire going. Everything is taken care of for the day."

Cora said, "No, we gathered coal from along the railroad tracks."

Mrs. Johnson said, "I'm so proud of you children for being resourceful and not bumming coal from a neighbor. Let's have our morning prayer and finish our daily devotions."

Mrs. Johnson was a pretty dark-haired woman with a little girl. Her husband worked in Chicago and wanted her to move up there with him. She lived with her mother who babysat her daughter, Belle. Her husband rented a large house and bought furniture for it, but Mrs. Johnson refused to move. She didn't want anyone taking care of Belle except her mother.

He said, "You can get another babysitter to take care of her. You can teach there, too."

Mrs. Johnson said, "No, I won't go and leave Mama."

Later they divorced, and both remarried. Mrs. Johnson married a soldier, but they divorced later as well because he too wanted her to move away from her mother.

* * * *

As Cora aged, her mother made all kinds of mean accusations about her. She kept saying that Cora was having sex, or if her period was late that Cora was pregnant.

Bertha would ask, "Okay, have you been hanging out in the bushes with boys? You know how boys want to brag about sex with girls. It will give you a bad name and people will look down on all of us."

No matter how much Cora denied it, her mother kept saying hurtful things to her. She wasn't allowed to date or go to church or any school activity at night. She wanted to go to her school's cake walk or pie supper, but Bertha seemed to take delight in being in complete control.

Cora Allen and Joey Johnson

When Cora was still in High School, she was in class with a boy named Joey Johnson. He was the teenage son of Lovey and Rod Johnson. By talking, they learned that they had a lot of things in common. They both liked to sing, act in plays at church, and listen to sports on the radio. They also both liked to hang out in the natural environment where they lived. The scenery was very beautiful in their area of Appalachia. He claimed Cora Allen for his girlfriend. One day, Bertha and Cora's Aunt Lily were looking out the window and saw the couple talking.

Bertha got very angry and stormed, "Here, Lily, take this baseball bat and knock him on the head and get him away from Cora."

Lily replied, "Ah, it's alright. Cora has a good head on her shoulders. And she can't get married until she's twenty-one anyway. By then it will all blow over. She knows his parents drink like fishes. You're worrying over nothing."

Since Cora wasn't allowed to date, Joey wrote notes to her telling about his life and feelings for her. It was mainly cute funny stories, with "XXX's" and" "OOO's" on the paper just before he put his name. Cora passed notes to him commenting on the note she had received the day before.

One evening Cora was reading his note that she had received that day. She thought that she was alone in the house, but her mother Bertha tiptoed inside and peeked around the door into the kitchen to see what Cora was doing. She saw Cora read the note, hastily fold it, and put it in her pocket.

Bertha was sly in some ways. She didn't let Cora see her. She knew Cora would hide the note somewhere before her skirt was washed. Bertha tiptoed back outside and noisily entered the house.

She said, "Tomorrow is wash day, get your dirty clothes ready. That skirt is looking dirty; be sure to put it in the laundry basket too."

Cora realized she had to act quickly to hide Joey's note. If Bertha found it, there would be terrible accusations made about its contents. She went into her room, took the note out, and put it in her shoe. She took her dirty clothes down to Bertha.

Cora sensed something was amiss by Bertha's facial expression and actions. Rarely did she ask for clothes the day before she did the laundry. Cora thought, "Does she know I have a note from a boy? I'll have to find a better place for this and the other notes he's given me. I'll hide them in the smokehouse, in the saltbox container. She won't think to look up there."

Cora went to school the next day while Bertha did laundry and searched every inch of Cora's room. Then she expanded the parameter of her search. She started on the outbuildings one by one. At last, she searched the smokehouse and found the notes.

When Cora arrived home, she saw all of Joey's notes unfolded and lying on the kitchen table. When she looked at Bertha there was an expression between a smile and a sneer on her face.

Her eyes had a glint in them that said, "Aha! I've gotcha!"

Bertha stormed, "Those teachers ought to be fired letting you get such garbage at school. Don't you have any better things to learn or do up there? You know that Johnson family; they're all a bunch of drunks! If that's what's going on, I might as well keep you at home!"

Cora said, "Mom, what have you done? Those were harmless private notes that he wrote to me just in fun."

Bertha yelled, "What about those "XXX's" and "OOO's"? Are you hugging and kissing him? Are you having sex with him? Is that why your time is late this month? Are you pregnant?"

With tears running down her cheeks Cora said, "No! No! No! I've not done anything! Why don't you leave me alone and stop accusing me of doing bad things!"

Bertha stormed, "Young lady, this is the last time that you get one of those notes! If I find another one, I'll take you out of that school."

Cora believed her mother would really carry through with her threat, which would mean living like she was in jail. The next day she told Joey what happened. He was shocked by Bertha's actions. They continued writing notes to each other for a while, but Cora never took any of them home.

The flirtation soon ended, in part due to the objections of Cora's parents. Before long they both started liking other people. As it turned out, they were wrong about Joey's character. Despite his years of living with alcoholic parents, he developed strong morals of his own. Joey turned out well in life. He got married and moved to Virginia. The couple had four boys. By middle age, his wife died and he remained a widower.

* * * *

Cora continued living at home with her parents until she graduated high school at eighteen, and lost her Social Security check. She suffered mental anguish practically every day from her parents accusing her of being a whore or of being pregnant.

Charles lived a double life. It was believed that he had another family some place. He stayed at home with Bertha only two or three weeks at a time. He spent about half of the day packing his things on his horse before he left for the next county. He even left when the crops needed tending. If he had a job over there, he never gave any money to Bertha or her children.

Perhaps Charles got his rambling ways from his mother but he did not follow the example she set as a hard worker.

June Allen

June was the mother of Charles Allen, and five other boys. June's six teenage boys were hard workers when they lived with June. Each winter June called several different places seeking summer work in different states. Because farmers needed laborers, it was easy for them to get jobs.

She would take her boys and six teenage neighbor boys with her to work. The farmers had bunkhouses for them to live in while they worked on their farms. One summer they rode a bus to Georgia to pick peaches. It was tiring hot work, but they were agile and fast at picking them. They also helped pack them for sale.

One time they went to Oklahoma on a bus to pick cotton. They spent three months working in the hot Oklahoma sun. They came back very tanned with pockets full of money. In New Jersey, they picked and processed asparagus. The weather was much cooler there which made it easy to do the work. June continued travelling for work until she had saved three thousand dollars, which she used to build a house with a block foundation on her in-laws' land.

Another time they rode a train to Idaho and harvested potatoes. The farmers drove huge tractors with big plows on them that drew the potatoes out of the ground. June, the twelve boys, and other workers put the potatoes in wagons. They had to be careful not to bruise them. Any potatoes that were cut had to be put in a special wagon. After they were gathered, the potatoes were washed, dried, and bagged to be sold.

After paying for her house, she continued working until she had enough money to fill her house with new furniture. She was very frugal and lived on a small amount of money during each assignment. It was said that June wasn't very smart, but she was a good manager.

Some of the boys continued travelling and harvesting crops for farmers in various states and during different seasons. They made good money for themselves and for their families.

* * * *

One day Charles came in from town and something made him angry. He saw Cora and grabbed her by the arm, swung her around, and slapped her hard on her face. Cora began crying from shock and pain. Her sign of weakness made him hit her again on her shoulder.

She managed to jerk herself free from his grasp and run off up the holler. She sat on an old stump crying and made plans to leave home.

Cora said aloud, "That's the last time."

Later she crept back to the house and went to bed without any supper. Before Cora went to sleep, she lay there praying and mulling over a plan of escape in her mind. The next morning, she rose early, helped cook breakfast, and ate without looking at Charles or Bertha. After breakfast, she washed the dishes and swept and mopped the kitchen floor. Her family was going to a funeral of a relative that day. Cora was going to stay home and cook dinner (midday meal). After they left, she got hot water, washed her hair, and took a sponge bath. Next she packed some of her clothes, her dress slippers, and biscuit sandwiches in a cow-feed sack and walked out of the house without looking back.

The Abusive Husband

Gertie – another of Cora's sisters – had left home before to escape the abuse. She did not however find peace in her new life.

When Gertie Allen got married, she and her husband Ira moved to Indiana to work in a canning factory. Ira was a mean man who drank. He had wrecked his car and killed his first wife. Gertie's mother, Bertha, begged her not to marry him. Bertha knew the family, how they lived, and the way their men treated their wives.

Ira packed, labelled, and filled cans into boxes. Gertie worked on the machine that filled the cans with cooked vegetables and fruits during their growing season. They canned anything else that the factory contracted them to do.

Gertie was pregnant when she got married. As time went by she began to show more. She had to miss work her last three weeks before Faye was born. They got behind paying their bills and Ira ranted and raved at her, claiming she was able to work. As soon as she had recovered, Gertie had to work a different shift from Ira so one of them could stay with Faye. Because Gertie wasn't there to breastfeed her baby, they had to feed her with a bottle. They continued working different shifts until Faye was weaned.

Being apart was taking a toll on their marriage. To make matters worse, Gertie's mental and physical health began to deteriorate from Ira's abuse. They talked it over and decided to take Faye to stay with Gertie's parents, Charles and Bertha, at their house. They didn't trust anyone in Indiana to babysit her. Also, Gertie's baby sister Cora was two years old and they could play and grow up together.

Faye developed impetigo on her hands and between her fingers. Bertha made a salve of grease and sulfur and rubbed it on Faye's hands. Bertha sewed mittens out of an old pair of men's long underwear and had Faye wear them at night to keep the salve from getting on the quilts. Her hands were healed in about a week, but the black scars remained for a few months.

Each year the factory shut down for two weeks to change from canning one product to another. During this time, Gertie and Ira would bring Faye to Indiana to visit. Other times, they would use the switchover break to visit family in Appalachia. Occasionally, they would use their weekend to go to see Faye as well.

Faye always wanted to stay in Appalachia with Aunt Cora and her grandparents. The girls had a playhouse in the barn loft and they spent many happy hours there pretending they were grown-ups with families. One of Cora's brothers built them a special log house on his parents' farm up the hill from Cora's house. It was 16x16 with two windows, carpet on the floor, and mud chinking between the logs. He put two beds in it too. They really enjoyed this special place. Some of their happiest times were spent there away from abusive parents and the negativity that had been prevalent in their young lives.

When Faye was three years old, Gertie got pregnant and gave birth to Reda Jane. Gertie had to take time off from work for several weeks. Ira's abuse became a lot worse after the baby's birth. They had to rotate shifts again for several months until Reda Jane was weaned. Ira thought Gertie got pregnant so she could take off work, and he didn't want to have to change his shift to take care of Reda Jane. Gertie had many bruises on her body and often had black eyes.

Once, an old lady saw Gertie's black eyes and said, "Whatever you want, you won't find it in a man." She meant that Gertie would have to find it within herself.

Reda Jane was soon brought back to Appalachia to live with Faye, Cora, and Cora's parents. When Faye was about ten, she went to Indiana for a visit. Her parents left her at home with Aunt Mae and her boyfriend. Aunt Mae went out to the store for snacks and beer. While she was gone, the man raped Faye and told her if she said anything, he would tie her up in a bag and throw her in a river. Faye was terrified and believed he would really drown her.

When she came back to Kentucky, she would wake up with crying spells at night. Sometimes she cried until she finally dropped off to sleep again. They asked her what was wrong but she would never tell anything. She may not have really remembered what happened. She may have blacked it out; but she was still scared.

One night after being disturbed, Bertha took the razor strap and whipped Faye. She told her to stop crying and waking everybody up. As time went on, Faye and Reda Jane moved back to Indiana where they attended high school. They both got married and had children of their own. Faye had two boys, and later divorced her husband. The boys went to live with their father.

As she got older, Faye lived on a farm and ran a small grocery store. Her two sons came back after their father's death and helped with the farm and the store. Faye developed Alzheimer's which grew progressively worse until she no longer knew anyone.

Aunt Mae married a fifty-two-year-old man that drew a V.A. check, who treated her well and she never had any children. After her husband died, she lived by herself in their house until her death.

Reda Jane had to help raise an extremely mentally challenged grandson named Joe. Almost every waking moment he tormented her. As he got older, he woke her up each night laughing hysterically, thinking it was a funny prank.

One day they were in the backyard. Joe sprayed her with the water hose and burst out laughing. Reda Jane had put on a new outfit and was going to go shopping shortly. Reda Jane snapped! She grabbed a pistol out of her purse and shot Joe, then shot herself. A neighbor had been in his back yard and saw the killing and the suicide.

* * * *

Cora walked across the hill and continued on for a few miles until she came to an abandoned two-room log cabin. She went in and saw that it was a mess, with things scattered all over the floors. There was a yellow bench in one corner that you could sit or lie on. She walked next door to the neighbors and talked to them about the house. It was an old couple named Metcalf.

Cora asked, pointing to the abandoned cabin, "Who owns that?"

Mr. Metcalf, sweeping his arm towards his aged wife answered, "Me and Patsy own it and another old store building on the highway down there. We ran it until we got too old to take care of it. It would make a good living for someone if they would take it over."

Patsy said, "We thought about selling used clothes in it at one time. Our preacher knows a place in Louisville where they give things away."

Cora asked, "Can I stay in the house if I help clean up the place? I'll help you get in water, mow the grass, chop wood or anything else you need me to do. Because my family was so mean to me, I've left home for good and I need some place to stay."

Mr. and Mrs. Metcalf, who were named Jim and Patsy, were touched by her situation.

Patsy said, "You poor child, let me make you some dinner. You must be tired and hungry. Once you've eaten you'll feel better, and we can talk things over."

As they ate, the three discussed a plan for Cora to stay in the cabin to work for her rent. They had been planning to fix it up and rent it out but they couldn't get anyone to help with the renovation.

The Metcalfs gave her a broom, a mop, a bucket, some rags, and a jug of water to drink. They agreed to let her live there if she worked and fixed up the house. Cora chopped wood, built a fire in the fireplace, and started burning trash in it. She collected items that couldn't be burned and dumped them in a nearby sinkhole. A tired Cora swept and mopped the floor with creek water, and used the rags to dust and wash all the walls that she could reach.

That evening she ate her biscuit sandwich and drank water for her supper. Cora pulled the bench close to the fireplace. Cora wept and prayed to God for guidance. Afterward she felt comforted and at peace with her situation and plan for the future. She lay on the bench for a bed and drifted off to sleep watching the flickering fire dance as it cast a soothing glow over the room.

A cold and stiff Cora was awakened the next morning by a wren singing outside the door. It had gotten cooler in the night. The once roaring fire had almost gone out and the room had chilled. She rose and stumbled over to the fire place where she dug around in the coals with a stick of wood. Upon finding some live coals, Cora gathered some paper and small pieces of wood to rekindle the fire. As the flames grew taller and hotter she put larger pieces of wood in the fireplace. She still had one biscuit sandwich left. After eating it she went to Jim and Patsy's house. They insist that she eat some hot sweetened oatmeal and drink a glass of milk.

After the meal, Cora washed the dishes and swept and mopped the kitchen floor. She put water in their Speed Queen washing machine so Patsy could wash Jim's clothes and her own. Cora hung them outside on the clothesline to dry.

Cora said, "Would it be possible for me to rent the old store building? I thought over what you said about the store and the preacher. Maybe the preacher and I could work out a deal where he could bring clothing to the store and I could sell them."

Patsy responded, "We'll need to go talk to the preacher and see if he would agree to this."

Cora replied, "I'd give him half of the profits. It would make money for me and for the church both. Also, would it be alright for some other girls to live with me and help with the work on the house and in the store? I promise we won't have noisy parties or any alcohol here. We're all girls that need to get away from our home because of mistreatment, either physical or mental."

Jim spoke up and said, "As long as everyone works, and you all keep your promises. It will be good to have someone live close to us. Since we are getting older and can't do the hard work or fix the house up, it seems it will be beneficial for everyone involved."

Cora asked, "Is it alright if I use your telephone to call the girls?"

Patsy and Jim answered in unison, "Yes, go ahead. It's in the front room by the fireplace."

Bossy and Fido

Although it wasn't common, some girls from very poor families had to work outside the home in order to bring in extra income. In many cases, this gave young women a degree of independence that wasn't common to the time and place.

In Appalachia, Judy Bledsoe was a young woman of seventeen who gave birth to a daughter, Mary, out of wedlock. She was overwhelmed by the responsibility of raising a child by herself. She signed up for public assistance soon after Mary was born. A few months later she met a sixty-year-old man that had eight grown children. His wife had been dead for five years.

Ray was a retired coal miner living on a pension. Since Judy was looking for security for herself and baby Mary, she agreed to marry him. He adopted little Mary and treated her and Judy well. He built a shotgun house. The first room was a kitchen. The next room was a living room, and at the end of the house were two bedrooms with a bathroom.

Judy learned to cook well. She was so proud of her new house that she kept it clean like a showpiece. Little Mary thrived with good food and the love of her parents. When Mary was about four, Judy gave birth to a son named Lonnie. Mary loved Lonnie dearly, and he idolized her. Soon the children were in school where they did well. When she was a teenager, Mary went to work in the general store for an old couple. She worked the cash register after school and on Saturdays.

She swept the floor and porch of the store and stocked the shelves. After she had her driver's license she delivered groceries. She earned twelve dollars a day from her work.

Mary was very popular with the customers and young men in the community. She worked in the store until she was about twenty-two. While she worked, she bought all kinds of things such as a bicycle for Lonnie, and material for kitchen curtains and pillows for their home.

In her work she met a forty-five-year-old man named John Jackson that was wealthy according to the income of most people in the area. He had eighty acres of bottom land that grew corn and other crops. He grew strawberries and sold them at a significant profit. He had a large apple orchard that produced a sizeable income each year, as well as a tobacco crop that brought in a substantial check for Christmas each year.

There was only one major thing wrong with John. He had been married four times and was divorced. His former wives said that he was insanely jealous and that they couldn't live with him. He started flirting with Mary each time he came in the store. Mary was excited that he paid her attention. Soon they began dating and he started talking marriage. Mary took him seriously.

Mary had a little dog named Fido that was a mutt. Although he was fully grown, he was still small. She also had a Jersey cow named Bossy. A neighbor had given Bossy to Mary as a small calf. That day, Mary had brought Bossy home in a wheelbarrow. Now,

Bossy was a cow that gave a lot of rich creamy milk. The family had nourishing milk and butter to drink and eat.

Mary's parents and Brother Lonnie begged her to break up with John. Mary kept seeing him and they got married a few weeks later in April.

Mary quit her store job and spent all of her time cooking, cleaning house, and helping with selling spring and summer items from the farm. Mary had brought Bossy and Fido with her when she got married. Each weekend, she took milk and butter home to Judy, Ray, and Lonnie in her new car that John had bought.

Everything went well for a few months, but soon John started asking," Who was that man that blew his horn at you when you were outside?"

Mary said, "It was a former customer that I knew when I worked in the store."

John kept saying all kinds of things, accusing her of having sex with any man that he could think of, including the old man that she had worked for in the store.

Mary kept saying, "I didn't do anything with any of those men. If I had wanted them, I wouldn't have married you." As time went on, John's jealousy became worse. He became obsessed with it.

Mary kept saying, "If you don't stop, I'm going to leave you. And if I do, I don't want you coming asking me to come back. If you ask me, I'll get the law after you. I won't have you aggravating my family."

His jealousy continued on and on and Mary was getting very exasperated. She couldn't sleep and cried often.

John wanted to get an electric milker for Bossy, but Mary didn't want one. She told him, "It will take much longer to wash and sterilize it than it would take to just milk her by hand." John insisted that he was going to buy one anyway. One day he left to go to Louisville on business and to get the milker.

Mary realized he was never going to listen to anything she said, and that he was ruining her health and happiness with his jealousy. She knew her marriage of only a few months was over. She packed her clothes in two cloth bags and put on a hat and long-sleeved blouse to protect her from the sun. Mary found a sturdy stick to use for protection from dogs or other dangers along the road. She packed some sandwiches in a paper sack and laid her wedding ring on the kitchen table with a note telling John she'd left and was divorcing him. She warned him again not to come after her or she'd get the law after him. Finally, she gathered Bossy and Fido and started her journey home.

She led Bossy with a rope while Fido followed them. She had put paper in Bossy's cowbell so it wouldn't ring and draw unwanted attention. Mary put the paper bag with the sandwiches in the top of one of the cloth bags and tied them both together. Next she laid them over Bossy's back so each one dangled down on one of her sides. Mary started on her fifteen miles walk to home and happiness. She used the stick as a walking cane and a weapon against aggressive dogs from the houses she passed. If Mary saw a dog, she picked Fido up and held him while she slung the club at the other dog.

She stopped occasionally to drink from a spring and eat a sandwich, but kept on her course to reach home as soon as possible. When Mary came near to her parents' house, she took the paper out of Bossy's bell. Mary liked to hear it ring as Bossy walked. She wanted her family to hear it and know she was coming home.

Her parents and Lonnie were sitting on the porch after supper enjoying the cool of the evening.

Lonnie said, "What's that sound I hear? It sounds like Bossy's bell. I sure hope its Mary bringing Bossy and Fido home"

A little later he cried, "Mommy, Mommy, Daddy, Daddy! It really is them; I'm so happy. I sure did miss them!"

They all rushed out to meet Mary and all of them hugged her. Ray took Bossy to the barn and fed her while Judy fed Mary a good meal from their leftover supper. Grinning from ear to ear, Lonnie fed and watered Fido. Because they had already guessed why she left, no one asked her any questions.

Ray said, "We can't afford to pay for a divorce."

Mary answered, "That's alright. I stopped at the store and got my job back. I'll pay for it myself."

After Mary saved up some money, she went to a lawyer and filed for divorce. In the 1950s, a divorce wasn't very expensive. It cost her less than $100. After the divorce Mary lived with her parents and brother for a number of years. After her father died and Lonnie grew up and had his own home, she stayed with her mother until Judy died. Later she met a retired teacher and married him.

* * * *

Cora called three of her friends and they agreed to move over with her the next day. Jim got some furniture out of the barn loft and they all took it up to the clean cabin in his pickup truck.

They had two beds with coil spring mattresses and a wood and coal burning cook stove. They set up the stove and the beds in the little house. Mr. Metcalf had metal stove pipe and hooked it up from the stove into a special hole in the kitchen side of the chimney.

The kitchen had a hand operated pitcher pump from the well, and a sink with a drain pipe that let out in the back of the house. There was a shelf over the sink for a pantry.

Cora said, "As soon as we get working in the used clothing store, we'll pay you back for anything you bought for us. I need to talk to the preacher myself and see if we can work out this deal. If he will bring the clothes to the old store building, the girls will help me sell them."

Mr. Metcalf said, "I'll drive you over to the church where he is working on the roof and see what he says."

They got into his pickup and rode to the church. Reverend Bill Jasper was climbing down the ladder from painting the roof.

Jim said, "Brother Bill, I'd like to talk to you. This is Cora Allen. She has a plan, and it should make money for her and the church."

Brother Bill replied, "Glad to meet you, Cora; we always need money for things at the church. What's your idea?"

Cora answered, "I want to fix up the old store building over on the highway and sell used clothing in it. I want you to bring boxes of clothes to the store, and me and my friends will run it and give the church half of the money. I've heard you can get boxes of clothes for free from Louisville."

Brother Bill said, "Sounds like a good idea, we're having trouble keeping the church running. I've been praying for something that could keep us afloat."

He shook hands with them and said, "Let me know when the store is ready for clothing and I'll borrow a truck from one of the church members to bring a load back to you. I can also buy you some furniture up there and you can pay me back later."

Jim, Patsy, and Cora drove back to the Metcalfs' house. They went inside and Patsy made bologna sandwiches and brewed coffee for dinner. They went to town that afternoon and purchased building supplies, housewares, and food for Cora and the other girls. They also went by the rural electric company and filled out paperwork to have the old house wired for service. It would be a few days before the electricity would be turned on in the house.

At about noon the next day, three tired girls named Lizzie, Sue, and Jeanie arrived at the cabin. Cora had killed a chicken that Patsy had given her, and cooked it in a large cast iron kettle with dumplings. She also cooked sweet potatoes, cornbread, and pinto beans. Cora had the meal ready when they arrived. Lizzie was sixteen with coal black hair and dark brown eyes. She had recently miscarried a baby and her parents turned her out from home. She had to stay with friends or relatives, or anyplace that would take her in. She was tall and thin and red-eyed from crying over the last week.

Shirley Parmley

In that time and place, the stigma attached to becoming pregnant outside of marriage made life very difficult for many young women who found themselves in that situation, regardless of the circumstances leading up to it.

Shirley Parmley, the youngest of ten siblings, was born on a cold frosty morning in 1934. She had blue eyes and curly blonde hair. Since she was the youngest child, most of the others had grown up and moved out to start their own families. Shirley had to take on more and more tasks. She had to chop up poles of wood for the stoves and draw buckets of water from the well each day. As time passed, she became a beautiful teenager. When she was thirteen, Tommy Deaton cast his eyes on her and liked what he saw. Tommy was eighteen and far more experienced in life than Shirley. Soon he started making a habit of being in groups where she was.

Shirl, as she was called, was flattered by his attention. He started walking her home from church at night and coming by her house on Sunday afternoons. Each night, Tommy started pressuring her to have sex. He was more and more persistent. Shirley was afraid she'd get pregnant, but he promised to marry her if it happened. Eventually she agreed, and they had sex on the one occasion.

Her worst thought came to pass, and Shirley panicked when she learned she was pregnant. When she told Tommy the news, he stammered about being sorry and hurried away from her. The next day he volunteered for the army and was shipped to Korea after basic training. His family wouldn't give her his address. She felt helpless and betrayed. Her life became a nightmare. The shame in Appalachia at that time of being pregnant and not married was a torment for her.

Her family eventually learned the truth. When her siblings came home on Sunday for the noonday meal, they teased her unmercifully.

"Shirl who's your baby's daddy, hee hee?" they railed at her over and over, month after month.

When the baby was born, they got her a doctor, and so as to not hear her screams, the rest of the family slept in the barn's hay loft that night. Her baby was a beautiful little girl that she named Lucy.

Then, the teasing continued each Sunday, but they often used the word "bastard" in their smirking and taunting voices.

Shirl stayed home each Sunday, killed chickens and got them ready to fry. When her mother got home she put on an apron and started frying the chicken that Shirl had killed.

Her mother said, "Shirl honey, go chop some more wood and bring it to the house in the wheelbarrow. Then dig some taters out of the garden and bring in some more water from the well."

Her sister Joan laughed and taunted, "Yes, that's all you're fit for. Shirl, who's the father of your bastard?"

Shirl cried remorseful tears and went out and sat on the porch like the help might do. Often she didn't eat or she grabbed a piece of chicken and a biscuit and that was all she got to eat because of their teasing.

Shirl went to town and signed up to draw welfare. Since she couldn't get very much money if she lived in the house with her parents, Shirl fixed up the smokehouse with a bed, stove, and chest of drawers. She often went out there on Sunday when the torment became unbearable. Most of her time spent in the smokehouse, Shirl was praying and crying. She took Lucy and a plate of food to eat.

Once when Joan was antagonizing her, Shirl picked up an empty quart jar and hit her hard on the head causing Joan to spill her plate. Joan said "Why did you do that? You about knocked my brains out! See what a mess you made!"

Shirl yelled "If you don't stop, I'm going to break the stove wood, mop handles and broom handles over your head. Just you wait and see. I'm going to leave and never come back!"

The siblings were jealous because Shirl was drawing a welfare check and some Social Security from their father. Shirl's mother said, "You all leave her alone. She's a good girl, a good mother to little Lucy, and I don't know what I would do without her. I'm not able to do the hard work anymore. Your carrying on is killing me. Enough is enough! She's drawing a check and helping me with the money. Shirl is my child, too. If you don't stop I'd rather you didn't come."

Still, week after week, Shirl stayed home, made beds, washed breakfast dishes, killed the chickens and they continued bothering her after church. Once or twice when Tommy Deaton was on furlough, he came by and saw little Lucy. If his parents hadn't been so set against him marrying Shirl, they might have had a good life together.

One Sunday morning, Shirl washed up the breakfast dishes, made beds, and swept and mopped the kitchen floor. She packed some of her and Lucy's clothes in a bag with cold biscuits and hog belly sandwiches and tucked the bag under her arm. With her other arm she led Lucy by the hand, walked out the door, and never looked back.

They walked a long way. When Shirl saw a pickup truck going her way, she hitched a ride. She put the bag in the back and nussed- or sat- Lucy on her lap. The strangers were going to a town out of the county. She told them a lie, that she had an aunt living near there. So she rode with them to that town.

After she got there, she and Lucy ate the biscuits and hog belly sandwiches. Later they got a drink from a spring along the roadside as they continued walking. The next ride they got was with an old couple named Sarah and John Martin. Because she was tired and sleepy, Lucy was crying and Shirl was worn out from walking and the weight of the bag of clothes. Shirl blurted out her circumstances to Sarah and John.

They were good country people that believed in helping unfortunate folks. Sarah and John told her that they wanted to help her. They had a small two-room house back of theirs. They agreed to let her move into it.

John had been a truck driver and he knew a place in Louisville that gave away furniture. The next day, he took his truck up there and brought back enough for her house and some other people in the community. They bought wallpaper for Shirl, which she pasted to the walls. She had a stove in the middle of the house that was used for cooking and heat for the winter. She had a table, chairs, a pitcher pump that brought water into the house, and a cupboard. In the bedroom she had a bed, a dresser with a mirror, a chest of drawers, and two padded chairs for sitting. The local church gave clothes to her and Lucy. Shirl changed her welfare check to her current address and got food stamps that provided them food. She worked for John and Sarah that summer and grew a big garden. Wherever Shirl worked, she took Lucy with her.

She canned or dried vegetables and fruit for John and Sarah as well as for herself, to eat in the winter. Shirl went to church with John and Sarah and to the town of Price where they shopped. Shirl bought a ton of coal each summer month until she accumulated enough for the winter. She learned to manage her money.

Three years later, on a Saturday when she was shopping with John and Sarah, Shirl walked down the street and one of her brothers saw her. He ran up to her and demanded to know where she'd been and told her that she needed to come back home. Shirl told him "I'm happy where I'm at. I have people that treat me good and I live in a house that I love. I'm never coming home."

A week later, her parents came to persuade her to come home. Her mother said "I've missed you and I'm not able to do much work anymore. I also miss the extras that you bought with your check."

Shirl answered, "Why don't you get Joan and the others to help you? You and pop wouldn't make them leave me and Lucy alone. If you'd both really put your foot down, they'd have stopped. I like it here and I'm never coming back." After many tears and begging Shirl to come home, Shirl's parents left and went back home.

When Lucy was old enough to go to school, Shirl rode the bus with her the first day. She stayed all day and made sure Lucy would be alright. Soon Lucy happily rode the bus and made friends with the kids on the bus and in her classroom.

Soon Shirl met Sarah's and John's grandson, Jesse. They dated a short while before they got married and moved back to another area of her native county. They never went around any of Shirl's family. Jesse gave Lucy his name and they had three other children that grew up not knowing any of their kinfolks.

Shirl and Jesse were good parents that reared their family to be honest, God-fearing, hard-working individuals. They did well in life. Jesse died when he was seventy-five years old. Shirl is eighty-five and still drives a car. She was born Appalachia tough. It means she conquered many obstacles in her life. She held fast to her faith in God and his promises. She knows God is a promise keeper. The generosity of John and Sarah Martin, God, and her welfare checks helped save Shirl and Lucy from starvation or some other calamity.

* * * *

Eighteen-year-old Sue was short and slightly plump with brown hair and blue eyes. She was a hard worker and had a survivor attitude. Her father had beat her every time he saw her talking to a boy.

The Joy Ride

The switch or the razor strap was all too commonly used as a way to drive home a message. What we call beating your child today was once called teaching discipline. This trend of course had long-lasting traumatic effects on children from this time and place.

A young man that worked in Ohio bought a newer used car and gave the old one to his fourteen-year-old brother Edgar. Edgar believed a car was supposed to always run fast and give him thrills. He drove it up and down the holler on the country dirt roads at speeds of sixty or seventy mph. He was dating a fourteen-year-old girl named Jane that lived near him. She was thrilled to be riding in the car with him instead of walking. She liked the special attention that she was getting.

Some of the neighbors wanted to call the police and stop them from killing themselves or someone else. Other people believed the kids should be able to have fun and that the others should just leave them alone.

Jane's mother said, "If you don't stop, you're going to get a bad name."

Jane sassed, as she stormed out of the house, "I bet you didn't have such a good name before you got married."

Her mother got very angry about the remark. She went outside and cut a big hickory switch. When Jane came home, she was beaten with it.

Her mother said, "Young lady, you'd better not say anything like that to me again, and if you don't start minding me, next time it will be a stick of stove-wood." Jane became more obedient and made Edgar stop driving so fast.

* * * *

Seventeen-year-old Jeanie was small with blonde curly hair and green eyes. Jeanie was smart and had done well in school. Her parents drank often and fought each time they got drunk. Jeanie worried about them and wanted to escape the turmoil.

The Drunks

Alcoholism would often grip every adult member of a family and wreak havoc on their ability to function as parents. This issue was all too common in this time and place.

Rod Johnson worked on the railroads and provided well for his family of fourteen children. He made sure they were well-dressed and attended the local schools. It took a lot of money to care for all of them. He was handsome and very masculine looking, but every weekend he got drunk. His wife, Lovey, was a good cook and housekeeper. She also was an educated woman, well dressed and good looking. Most weekends when her husband drank, Lovey joined him and got sloppy drunk, too. She would lay sprawled out on the floor, and her children would cover her so her bottom wasn't exposed. It was believed that Lovey got drunk only to spite her husband. When she wanted to, she could stay sober, and put drinking aside. Later in life she became a Christian and stopped it completely.

At eighteen, Gloria Johnson was one of the older children who hadn't left home yet. Gloria did a lot of housework and cooking. She also helped take care of her younger siblings, especially when her mother got drunk.

One day, her two-year-old brother Johnny was whining, and a friend asked, "What's wrong with him?"

Gloria said, "Just wait and see."

She got some potatoes, peeled and fried them in a cast iron skillet. When they cooled, she put Johnny in his high chair and gave him milk and potatoes to eat. He ate every bit of them. Johnny was hungry, and Lovey wasn't in any condition to take care of him.

One of Gloria's older sisters, Debbie, was pregnant and about to give birth. Early one morning Gloria packed a few items in bag along with some biscuits and fried side meat. She started walking on the long trek to Debbie's house in another community. If a car stopped and asked her to ride, Gloria refused. She was afraid someone would hurt her so she kept walking. She ate two biscuits and meat that day and drank spring water along the road.

That night she slept in an abandoned building. The next morning she ate another biscuit sandwich and drank water from a fast-moving creek that she came upon. She had worn a straw hat and long-sleeved shirt for protection from the sun. She was still tired from walking the day before and from sleeping on a hard floor last night, but she trekked on and on. She arrived at Debbie's house late that night and knocked on the door.

Debbie hugged Gloria and said, "I'm so happy to see you! I've been worried about how I'm going to take care of my three babies and my newborn too."

Gloria said, "You don't know how glad I am to finally get here. I'm worn out and I need something to eat and a bed to sleep in. Tomorrow I'll feel better and can help you with everything."

She ate and went to bed where she slept very soundly. The next morning a little child woke her up by tickling her nose with a feather. She quickly got dressed and rushed to help with the breakfast preparation. After the meal was over, she started cleaning the whole house. She only stopped a few minutes to eat dinner that she'd cooked, and continued working.

A few days later, Debbie had her fourth baby. She and her husband named him Randy. He weighed seven pounds and was twenty-one inches long.

Gloria stayed a month and worked hard each day. She cooked meals, cleaned house, and washed and ironed the family's clothes. Finally when Debbie was stronger from Randy's birth, Gloria said, "I'm going home tomorrow. I'll leave early in the morning to walk home."

Debbie said, "We'll take you home, but we sure wish you could stay. You've been a lifesaver for us."

Gloria answered, "I'm needed at home; Mom and Pop need me to help with the house and children."

The next day, they all piled into the station wagon and drove to Gloria's home.

Gloria continued being a good sibling to her brothers and sisters. She was always cheerful and sang a lot when she worked. About two years later, she met a handsome young man and married. Later, she had three children. She took care of them and had a happy marriage, but there weren't any alcoholic beverages allowed in their home. Now her family is very active in their local church.

* * * *

Cora hugged Jeannie, Lizzie, and Sue and said, "I'm so happy to see you all. Come in. I have dinner cooked."

The girls sat around the kitchen table and enjoyed the delicious meal. They smiled at each other and felt at peace.

Lizzie looked at the other girls and said, "Life's a heavy load when no one loves you. I felt so scared and alone for the last few weeks. I've really learned my lesson. I'll be careful what boy I get involved with again. When Cora called, it was like an angel was looking out for me."

Sue said, "I'm so glad she called me too. I'm black and blue all over from being whipped. No matter what I said, Dad wouldn't ever believe me. I'll work so hard to get to stay and live in peace. "

Jeanie spoke up with tears running down her cheeks, "My life has been a living hell. My Mom and Pop were always drinking and fighting. I had to walk on eggshells around them when they were drinking. I had to dodge things they threw at me more times than I can count."

Cora spoke, "You all know my story. I couldn't stay there anymore either. Between getting beat and getting accused of being pregnant all the time, no one can live like that."

Ruthie Allen

Sam Allen's daughter Ruthie, Cora's niece, lived in Chicago. She had become pregnant before she was married. She decided to have an abortion; since they lived in a major city, there was an abortion clinic not too far away. She went into the building and was almost ready for the procedure. To the doctor's amazement, she had a pang of guilt, got up and left.

Ruthie looked in the telephone book for the address of an unwed mothers' home, caught a bus and checked herself into the facility. She stayed until her baby was born. Ruthie was supposed to give the baby up for adoption. She asked the nurse to allow her to see the baby. Upon seeing and holding her, Ruthie changed her mind about giving her up.

She took the baby home and soon got a job to support it. Later, she got married and had four more children. Her husband adopted her little girl and they continued living in Chicago.

* * * *

Cora continued her speech to the girls, "We can have a fresh start here. The Metcalfs are going to buy materials to fix up this log cabin, but we have to do the work. He's old, but he can tell and show us what to do. After the cabin is fixed, we need to clean up his old store building and sell used clothes in it. Brother Bill, the local preacher, will go to Louisville and get them for free. He's also going to buy some used furniture to help furnish our house. He's going to buy us a chest of drawers, a table with chairs, and a refrigerator. We will have to pay him back, five dollars a week from each of us. But the most important thing is that we must work for Jim and Patsy to pay our rent. They are old and it's the least we can do since they have set us up in the shade. We have to behave to stay here: no alcohol, loud parties, or sleeping with boys."

The girls all nodded their heads signifying that they would work and live by the rules, and they even signed a contract that only the four of them would live in the house. They all joined hands and shouted, "Yes!"

That afternoon, Mr. Metcalf drove his pickup up to the cabin. It was loaded with sawhorses, tools, and lumber to replace the porch floor. He sat in a chair and told them how to use crowbars to remove the old rotten boards. They used one of the boards to measure the length for the new ones. He had them count how many boards they would have to cut, and took turns sawing the new lumber to the correct length. When one girl was sawing, the other girls were nailing the new ones into place. By that evening they had a new porch floor.

They were tired and hungry when they sat down to their leftovers supper. They ate heartily and washed it down with water. After eating they got ready for bed. Cora slept with Sue and Jeanie while Lizzie occupied the other bed.

The next day the girls cooked and ate breakfast early. They made their beds and washed their dishes.

Lizzie looked out the window and said, "Here's Mr. Metcalf. He sure is early this morning. I guess it's time we get to work on the house." They rushed outside and saw him unloading a ladder and rolls of green tar paper.

"Morning, girls", he said.

"Good morning, Mr. Metcalf," they said in unison. "What are we working on today?"

"Well, if it rains that roof could leak. I brought you some new tar paper so you all can fix it up before that happens."

Susan asked, "What do we need to do first?"

Mr. Metcalf answered, "Well, one of you needs to climb up to the roof, and another hand up the roll of tar paper. You have to unroll it and measure the width of the roof, then cut the tar paper that length. Throw down the strip and use it to measure more strips like it."

Sue climbed the ladder first and Cora carried the heavy tar paper up the ladder. The two girls started unrolling the paper from one edge of the roof to the other. Sue cut the tar paper at the desired length and threw it to the ground.

Jim yelled, "Throw the rest of the roll down so we can cut the other pieces!"

After the girls threw the roll down, Jim and Lizzie started cutting more pieces. Lizzie took one piece up the ladder, came back down, got a hammer and big headed roofing nails, and took them up to the other girls. One girl held the tar paper in place while the others nailed it in place starting at the eves of the house. They lapped a second piece over the top of the first one. It was slow work nailing and lapping piece after piece and covering the whole roof. Occasionally they switched jobs, nailing and holding the tar paper. Lizzie cut more pieces as they were needed and took them up one at a time. Last of all, they put a cap on the top of the roof with a final piece of tar paper.

By late evening the roof was covered, with only a few short breaks for dinner, going to the toilet, or getting drinks of water. The tired group of girls cooked a quick supper of sausage, scrambled eggs and light bread washed down with the Metcalfs' well water. They sat on the porch floor and talked about their plans for the future. Soon lightning bugs started floating up in the twilight sky and a chorus of frogs started singing a melodious evening song. In the distance a lonely rain crow started calling for rain and its mate. Soon the girls stood up and went inside to bed. Their aching muscles didn't even keep them awake that night.

The next day, Jim Metcalf arrived with a long rope, a bucket, a hoe, a small shovel, and a gallon of bleach.

Lizzie laughed and said, "What on Earth are we going to do with all of these things?"

He said, "Gals, it's time to clean out that well yonder. I'll tell you all how to do it. I don't want you all getting sick from drinking that water. We'll put the ladder in the well, one of you go down in it and fill up this bucket with water. If you hit mud, you'll need to pull that out too. The well is walled up, but it's hand dug so there's liable to be some muck at the bottom. Next you come back up while the other girls pull the rope and lift the bucket up out of the well. You can't stay down there while the bucket is coming out. It might fall and bump you on the head. You all can take turns doing the different jobs. You have to empty all the water out and then scoop out any gunk. Lastly, we pour bleach in the well to purify it."

Cora decided to go down into the dark damp well first. She was very careful as she descended the ladder one rung at a time. She yelled back, "Oh! This water is cold! It's gonna be tiring and hard climbing up and down this ladder with wet feet. It'll take many trips to get this well emptied and cleaned."

Cora dipped up a bucket of water and climbed out while Lizzie pulled up the bucket and poured it out away from the well.

They continued working and taking turns all afternoon until the well was emptied and all the mud was scooped out. When it was clean, they pulled up the ladder and poured bleach into the almost dry well.

Jim said, "Now you have to wait for the well to fill up. It'll taste bleachy for a while, but it won't make y'all sick. I'll take a sample to the health department and get it tested to make sure it's safe to drink."

Sue commented, "It will be good to have water this close to the house. At home I had to carry it a long way from a spring."

Jeanie and Lizzie agreed, "We did too."

After eating supper, the four girls went outside and lay on the grass beneath a maple tree in the front yard. As they lay there resting their aching muscles, Cora said, "Well, you know tomorrow's going to be another day of hard work. We'd better get some sleep."

"Let's wait a little longer. It's so nice out here this time of day," Jeanie responded.

Lizzie said, "I'm tired and sore, but I love it here with you all. I want to wait a little longer and soak up the coolness of the evening."

The girls started swapping stories and reflecting on their good fortune. It quickly became almost like a game, each girl trying to top the other with increasingly gruesome stories they had heard about the fates of women and girls in the places they had lived.

Jeanie kicked it off with a story she had heard about an old couple.

Hester and Harley

Hester and Harley Dean lived up a holler in Appalachia. Hester was a hard-working God-fearing woman in her seventies who was living on Social Security. Harley was also in his seventies. He drove an old car too fast for the conditions of the road. When he got drunk, all the neighbors could tell because he drove the car even faster.

Another side effect of his drinking was the physical and verbal abuse he inflicted on Hester. Many times she ran to a neighbor's house to escape Harley's wrath and hid there. One afternoon, without warning, Hester stormed through the back door of her nearest neighbor and dashed into their stairway closet to hide. She was panting loudly and very scared. Harley drove up and down the road looking for Hester. After Harley gave up finding her, he went home and went to sleep. Only then would Hester dare to return home.

Due to years of abuse, Hester had developed a nervous disposition. Because of this, even after Harley died, she still went to a neighbor's house during major storms. If the storm was at night, she would sleep on their couch until the storm was over, or even all night. She bought a trailer and moved in on a nephew's property where she lived until her death.

* * * *

Sue chimed in, "That's nothing; listen to this!"

The Death

Wilbur Pike was a farmer that owned some bottom land in Appalachia. He had one son and two daughters. He was a hard taskmaster toward his three children. They had many chores including feeding the animals and tending the crops. He was also very physically abusive to his children and his wife, Zella.

Zella was a meek, cowed-down woman. She and the children wore old, faded, and often dirty clothes. Many times the son, Lenny, had to run to get away from Wilbur's temper fits. When Wilbur's anger subsided, Lenny would come back. When Lenny was younger, his shorter legs couldn't carry him away from Wilbur's wrath. He learned the consequences that came with failing to escape.

His two daughters, Julie and Jan, had a different fear of Wilbur. He was sexually abusing them in the barn. He would corner them when he found them isolated, out doing the milking or other chores. He had outfitted the barn with a TV and a couch in one section, where the abuse took place.

Word got out in the community and Wilbur was charged with incest. When he went to court, his wife and son testified, corroborating the daughters' claims about the abuse. Because he had merchants swear that he was a good upstanding person in the community that paid his debts, he wasn't charged for the crime.

When Wilbur went home, he beat his whole family for swearing against him. He continued having sex with Jan and Julie. They were too afraid to refuse and just wanted to get it over with.

A short time later, Wilbur was mad at Lenny and beat him up before Lenny could escape. Lenny was bleeding and very angry at his father's mistreatment of himself and his family. Lenny had had enough. He went to the house, got the shotgun, and killed Wilbur.

Lenny had to go to prison, but his sentence was commuted due to the circumstances. When he got out of prison, he went home and worked on the family farm. He married a girl from another county and they made a good life together.

* * * *

The other girls gasped at the cruelty and violence of Sue's story. Lizzie, however, came forth with the most disturbing tale of the night.

The Baby

Lester James' family lived on top of a big hill in Appalachia. He had three sons and four daughters. He was a short pudgy farmer.

He was engaging in sex with two of his younger daughters. It wasn't known if that had happened with the two older daughters as well. One of them by the name of Wilma got pregnant. She was very upset and disillusioned by the whole experience of incest and the pregnancy. She hid at home and wouldn't go out in public to be seen.

When it came time for the delivery of Wilma's baby, a few of the neighborhood women gathered to assist in the birth. Wilma was young and scared. She had a very long and painful delivery. One of the women took the baby and started cleaning the blood from it.

Lester rushed in and snatched the newborn out of the woman's hands. He ran out of the room and outside the house. A few minutes later he came back into the house alone. The women were astonished and asked, "Where's the baby?!"

Lester looked them straight in the eyes and asked, "What baby?" The women ran outside to try to find it, but all they could see and hear were the hogs squealing and chomping.

When Wilma was able to travel, she and her sister went to Cincinnati to live with an older sister. They never returned home after that. Whenever they visited, they stayed at one of their brothers' houses. They met men in Cincinnati, married them, and continued living there.

* * * *

After an evening of sobering realization, the girls trooped into the house and retired for the night. They slept soundly until sunrise the next morning with a newfound sense of their own good fortune. They were awakened by a red-headed woodpecker tapping on an outside wall of their cabin.

Cora yelled, "Shoo! Shoo! You noisy rascal!"

Then she burst out laughing, "Who would have thought about a woodpecker waking us up?" The other girls laughed too.

"I'm tired but so happy with you all. No drunk is bothering me here," Jeanie said.

Sue chimed in, "I can laugh and be happy now. I don't have to worry about being whipped over nothing."

Lizzie said, "Since I've been with you all, I've gaining my strength back from the miscarriage, and it's so peaceful here. I've not cried once since I came."

"Yes, I am so glad you all moved in too," replied Cora, "Nobody here is accusing me of being a whore or pregnant if my time is late."

The girls ate breakfast, washed the dishes, made the beds, and swept and mopped the floors. Then they waited for Jim to come to tell them about the next job. Jim had measured the two windows in the building the day before. He came from town that afternoon having purchased new ones that were the same size. This morning he brought them to the cabin and showed the girls how to remove the old windows and install the new ones. In the winter they would cover the windows with clear plastic sheets. The girls took razor blades and removed any paper logos from the glass panes. Then they washed and dried the glass. They used white enamel paint to coat the wooden sections of the frames. He also had a tub, hoes, and buckets in the back of his truck.

After they finished installing and cleaning the windows he said, "Gals, let's go down to the creek in the holler and get some clay. You all can use it to 'chink', or fill in the spaces between the logs. 'Cause it's not been done for a few years, it's gonna take a lot of clay and work."

Two of the girls got in the cab and the other two sat in the bed of the truck. Once they left the main road, it was a bumpy ride. Each girl piled out of the truck, grabbed a hoe and a bucket. They waded barefoot into the cold water searching for bluish clay along the creek. Some of it was covered completely with water but an abundant amount was along the bank. They dug out chunks with the hoe and put them in their buckets. When their buckets were full they emptied them into the tub. They worked until the tub and all their buckets were filled.

Cora shivered, "Whee! I'm glad to get out of that icy creek for a while."

"Me too, I'm chilled to the bone!" Sue replied.

They started back to the cabin, where they used their bare hands to chink all the holes that the weather had loosened or washed away. Later Patsy Metcalf walked up to the cabin carrying an iron Dutch oven filled with chicken and dumplings for their dinner. They all wolfed down the delicious meal.

Cora said, "That really hit the spot. Thank you, Patsy, for such good food. That's my favorite thing to eat."

The other girls chimed in too, "Yes, thank you, Patsy, it was so good."

After dinner they continued chinking until they emptied the containers and went back to the creek for more clay. Lastly, they took turns climbing the ladder to get some of the top logs chinked. A happy but tired group of girls climbed into bed that night. They slept well until daylight; no woodpecker disturbed them that morning.

The girls had a potty chair that they used at night, and it was emptied in the outside toilet each morning. Daytime, they used the toilet when they had to go. The toilet had a bench seat with a hole cut in the top board. When they sat on the hole, the waste fell down into a pit. The toilet was covered with a metal roof. Because of the odor, it was an unpleasant place to visit.

They bathed in a large galvanized wash tub. After heating water on the cook stove, each girl would bathe in the filled tub. They staggered which night each girl would take a bath and wash her hair. Other times, they washed up with a pan of water and a washrag.

Jim came by early and said, "Do you gals want to bring your dirty clothes over to the house and wash them with Patsy's and mine? If you do, I'll wait and give you a ride over to the house."

The girls hastily gathered up their meager pile of dirty clothes and sheets and put them in a pillowcase. Then they rushed out to the truck with them. It was such a beautiful warm day that all the girls got in the back of the truck, and rode down to the Metcalfs' house. The Metcalfs had an electric wringer washing machine. Patsy had water boiling on the cook stove. Sue started dipping it out of the tub and pouring it into the washer. Lizzie cut up shavings of lye soap and dropped them into the washer to dissolve in the hot water. The other girls refilled the tub on the cook stove for the next load. They also poured some cold water in the washer so it wouldn't scald the person who was washing the clothes.

After sorting the clothes into piles by colors, they put some of them in the washer. The put the sheets and the light colored clothes in first. Next the pants and darker clothes were washed in the same water. Afterward they emptied the washer by letting the water drain out through the attached hose into buckets which the girls dumped out on the hillside. Next they refilled the washer and loaded it with the leftover sheets and light-colored things that did not get washed in the first load. Lastly, the pile that might fade was washed.

After each washing the clothes were put into a tub beside the washer, rinsed, and run through the wringer to get most of the water out of each piece. Sue rinsed and ran the clothes through the wringer. Lizzie took the wet clothes outside and hung them on a wire line with clothespins. Jeanie and Cora kept carrying water to the stove to heat and poured it with some cold water into the washer and rinse tub. Patsy was busy baking sweet potatoes and cornbread. She had green onions from her garden and a pot of soup beans, or pintos, to eat with milk to drink.

When the clothes got dry, the girls took them off the line and folded up the sheets, towels, and underwear. They took turns running a heated heavy metal iron over the folded clothes. The irons were placed on the cook surface of the wood stove. One was used for ironing while the other one was heating. The outer clothes were ironed last. Some better clothes were sprinkled with cooked starch; then the items were rolled up in a ball to evenly spread the moisture through the piece for a while before it was unrolled and ironed dry.

When the ironing was done, the girls put their folded clothes back in the pillow case and hung the outer clothes on wire hangers and walked back up to their house. They cooked supper before they went outside to listen to crickets, night birds and frogs for a while. They passed the time by telling jokes and stories.

Cora said, "Have you all heard the story of the Old Crow Man?"

Lizzie responded, "No I haven't. Please tell it to us."

"Okay, but settle in; it's a long one."

The Old Crow Man

Once upon a time, there was an elderly widow named Ruth who had three beautiful blonde daughters. They lived in an old cabin in the mountains. They had a garden each summer, and farm animals including horses, cows, chickens, and geese that helped provide them a living.

One day one of the geese was missing. Ruth said to her youngest daughter, Beth "Go out in the mountains and find that goose. I know she has stolen out her nest and is setting on the eggs to hatch. I need to know where it is so I can help take care of the goslings when they hatch."

Beth said, "All right, Momma, I'll find it for you."

She set off immediately and searched hither and yon, but she couldn't find the goose. As she grew tired, she didn't watch where she was walking. Beth fell down a deep hole into another land. It was so beautiful with blue streams of water, green grass, trees and flowers. Since she was tired and hungry, she hurried across the lush grassy fields looking for a house and something to eat and drink, and a place to rest.

Soon she came to a lovely mansion. She knocked on the door, and the weird-looking Old Crow Man answered it. He was a very large, strong man with a shock of jet black hair, a beard, and piercing dark eyes.

Beth said, "Please, kind sir, I'm so hungry and tired. May I have something to eat and rest a little while?"

"Yes, of course. Come in, come in," the Old Crow Man said as he smiled a wicked grin.

He had wonderful food for her to eat, several meats, vegetables and desserts. Since Beth got very sleepy, he showed her a beautifully furnished bedroom.

He said, "Rest a while before you start home."

Beth laid on the bed and drifted off to sleep. She awoke the next morning about eight o'clock. She jumped up and ran into the kitchen where he was eating breakfast.

The Old Crow Man said "Come join me; I just got started. There's plenty for both of us."

Since Beth was so hungry she eagerly sat down and ate a lot of food. She had gravy and biscuits, sausage, fried eggs, sweet cooked apples and some blackberry jelly on her buttered biscuits.

After she had eaten, the Old Crow Man asked, "Will you marry me?"

Beth answered, "No, I won't. I don't love you."

He grabbed her and locked her up in a huge beautiful gilded cage. He was kind to her and fed her very well each day and gave her lovely clothes to wear. He came to the cage every day and admired her beauty.

When Beth had been gone for a few days, Ruth called her middle daughter to her and said, "Caroline, I want you to go look for that wayward goose and my baby, Beth."

Caroline said "Yes, of course, Mother. I miss little Beth very much. I'll find them for you."

She started out that morning looking throughout the fields and mountains, but she couldn't find Beth or the goose anywhere. As she stumbled over a rock on one mountainside, Caroline fell into the same large hole as Beth. When she stood up and dusted herself off, Caroline saw the same scenic surroundings.

She started walking along, and soon she came to the same large ornately decorated house and knocked on the door.

When the Old Crow Man opened the door, Caroline asked, "Please mister, may I have something to eat and drink? I'm very tired from walking all around looking for my sister, Beth. May I rest a while?"

He answered, "Yes, young lady. Come in by all means. I've got plenty of good food for you to eat."

Caroline ate a plate full of delicious food and asked, "May I rest a while? I'm so tired."

The Old Crow Man took her to the same bedroom and said, "Lie down and rest before you start home."

Caroline was so tired that she slept until the next morning. When she woke, she sat up with a jerk and jumped out of bed. She walked to the kitchen and saw a table laden with all kinds of breakfast food.

When the Old Crow Man saw her, he said "Come in and pull up a chair and sit a spell. I've got breakfast ready. Eat until your heart's content."

Caroline ate a hearty breakfast because she was very hungry. She was partial to gravy and biscuits and had two servings. She finished off her meal with a piece of rhubarb pie.

The Old Crow Man asked, "Will you marry me?"

Caroline gasped and answered, "No. I don't love you."

He grabbed her and locked her in the cage with Beth. He was very kind to them, but he kept them locked in the cage at all times.

After a few more days had passed and Caroline didn't come back, Ruth called her oldest daughter to her side.

"Dorcas, I'm desperate and worried. Go and find my girls. Don't bother looking for the goose. She'll come home soon with a bunch of goslings trailing behind her. Be very careful. I don't want to lose you too. I'll starve to death if you don't come back. You know I'm too old to care for myself now."

Dorcas left immediately and started searching for her younger sisters. She walked until she became very weary. She started to sit down on a ledge on the mountainside and fell into the same hole.

Shakily, she scrambled to her feet, and looked all around at the new things she saw. Dorcas admired the beauty of the place and set off to explore it. Soon she came to the same large fabulous house. She knocked on the door twice, and heard someone coming to the door.

The Old Crow Man opened the door and stared at the pretty girl standing there. She had long blonde hair, smiling blue eyes and a very pretty face and pleasing form.

Dorcas asked politely, "May I come in and rest, I'm, very hungry from traipsing all over the mountains today."

The Old Crow Man replied, "Yes, of course. Do come in. I'm just about to eat supper. Won't you join me?"

Dorcas beamed, "I'd love to. You're so kind to take in a stranger."

After she'd eaten a large meal, he showed her the same lovely bedroom. She lay down to rest and Dorcas didn't wake up until the next morning. She stood up and straightened up the bed spread that she'd laid on that night before. Then she walked out into the kitchen, smelled, and saw the many bowls of foods that were on the table.

"Won't you join me for breakfast?" the Old Crow Man asked.

"Yes, I'd be delighted to. I'm sorry I didn't wake up sooner. I must have been very tired indeed," Dorcas said.

She ate mostly the different meats with a biscuit and some gravy. She chatted with him about the glorious country and his ornate house.

After the meal was over, the Old Crow Man asked, "Will you marry me?"

Dorcas sensed something was sinister about him and decided to keep him pacified until she knew what he intended. "Yes I will; I really love it here."

He said, "The circuit preacher is due to come by here in two weeks. We'll get married then."

Dorcas smiled and said, "Okay, that will be great. It'll give me time to get to know you better."

That night, she slipped out of her room, searched the house, and found her two sisters. She hugged them through the bars and said, "Don't worry, I have a plan to rescue you."

The next morning after breakfast, she said, "I'm so worried about my poor old mother. She must be starving while we have all this good food."

The Old Crow Man said, "Get some vittles ready and I'll take them to her. Here's a burlap bag that you can put them in. I'll pack it up to her house and leave it on her front porch."

Dorcas said, "Goody! I'll be a while. You go ahead and get yourself ready while I'm working."

After he left to go change she hurriedly went into the room with the cage, located the key and released Beth. She took Beth into the kitchen and put her into the burlap bag and tied it with a seagrass string.

When the Old Crow Man came to the kitchen, Dorcas said, "It's ready. I put a lot of good things in there, but don't open the bag or a lot of it will fall out."

He picked up the bag and started toward the front door.

Dorcas followed him and said again, "Remember, don't open the bag. My poor mother needs all the food that's in it."

As he walked down the road, he heard Dorcas yell, "Don't open the bag!"

He walked on and on. Eventually he set the bag down to rest a spell. He said out loud, "I wonder what she put in it. I can't believe how heavy it is."

He put his hands on the string.

Beth said from inside the bag, "Don't open the bag."

The Old Crow Man said, "Boy! Dorcas has a strong voice. I can hear her way out here."

He picked up the bag and trudged on.

Soon he had to rest again from the bag's weight. "I'll empty part of it out. Surely one old woman won't eat that much food."

Beth said again, "Don't open the bag."

He continued on. When he came to Ruth's house, he slung the bag around and flung it onto the porch. It bumped hard and slid against the wall. It hurt Beth but she didn't say a word or cry out.

While he was away, Dorcas made a life-sized cloth doll, stuffed it with straw, and dressed it in Beth's clothes. She put a hat on its head and put it in the cage with Caroline. She painted the doll's face to look like Beth.

When he got home, Dorcas had a large supper ready, too. He ate and smiled at her and said, "You will make me a good wife."

Two days later, Dorcas sobbed, "My poor, poor mother, she's eaten all that food by now and must have given up to starve to death."

The Old Crow Man said, "Since you are such a good girl, I'll take her some more grub. Get it ready while I bathe and change."

Dorcas got the key, let Caroline out of the cage, and put her in the burlap bag that he'd provided. She tied it up tight and said to him, "Remember, Mother needs all this food, so don't open the bag."

As he left the house walking she yelled. "Don't open the bag!"

She ran in, got the doll, put it in her own chair, and hurried after him at a distance. She was very careful so he wouldn't see her following him. Each time he set the bag down, Caroline said, "Don't open the bag."

He kept thinking Dorcas was yelling at him from his porch, so he picked it up and continued on to Ruth's house where he flung it onto her porch and left. Undetected, Dorcas came out from behind a large tree, ran upon the porch and untied the bag. A bruised Caroline crawled out and hugged Dorcas. They went into the cabin, shut the shutters, and barred the door.

When the Old Crow Man got home, he said to the life-sized doll, "Where's my supper?"

Since the doll didn't answer he yelled, "Get my supper or you'll know what for."

Still the doll didn't move. He started beating on it and the straw commenced scattering out of it. He realized that he'd been tricked, and he ran into the cage room and saw that it was empty. He knew that Dorcas and the girls were gone.

He charged out of his house, ran on and on until he came to Ruth's cabin. They had the shutters fastened and the door barred and they wouldn't let him enter. He beat on the door and yelled for them to let him in.

The Old Crow Man went out on the mountainside and cried and yelled until he popped open and that was the end of him.

* * * *

Lizzie spoke up and asked, "So that's it? He just popped open and died?"

The girls all laughed and called it a night.

A few days later the electric company came to the cabin and wired it for electricity. It took two or three hours to complete the task. It was wonderful to finally have bright lights to see how to work, or to sit up and talk, or work inside after dark.

Later that evening, Jim came to the cabin with a lantern and a rope to check that the chimney was safe and not a fire hazard. He had Cora climb up to the roof and attach the rope to the bail of the lit lantern. Next she slowly lowered it down the chimney and raised and lowered it up and down. Jeanie was stationed in the attic as Cora raised and lowered the lantern. She looked to see if she could see any light shining from between the rocks and cement of the chimney. She watched carefully from every angle and could not see even a glint of light. The chimney was safe to use and they could even build big fires in it on cold winter days.

Jim said, "I know this seems like a lot of extra work, but remember: safety first. I don't want to have a house fire up here and y'all lose your lives."

Each day the girls worked for the Metcalfs and on the cabin, either inside or out. They painted the outside logs brown, and the dried mud chinking was painted white. They were so proud of their handiwork. They underpinned the cabin with tin. There was a little door under the cabin. That summer, they raised and dug about twenty bushels of potatoes and stored them under the cabin. They also stored canned goods down there.

After removing the dirt dauber nests on the inside of the house, they covered the ceiling with sheets of white Styrofoam. They went to town with Jim and got cardboard refrigerator boxes, flattened them, and tacked them up on all the inside walls. Then they pasted newspapers onto the walls with homemade flour paste. Next the Metcalfs bought proper wallpaper for them to cover up the newspaper. It took about a month to get the house remodeled. Now they had a beautiful warmer cabin in which to live. In the meantime the four girls worked for Jim and Patsy at any job that needed to be done. They push mowed grass, cleaned house, did laundry, worked in the garden, and canned vegetables and fruits for the Metcalfs.

Their work paid the rent on the house and the store, which they would have up and running in a short time. They also worked for groceries and household items. Finally they got started on the store building. They dusted the shelves and counters, and washed the windows. Next they swept and mopped the floors.

Since it had been a store earlier, it already had shelving and counters from when Patsy had operated the store.

When it was clean, they contacted Reverend Bill Jasper at the church. Each Sunday they attended church and sang specials for the congregation. When they sang they wore black skirts and white blouses. Since they didn't have a car, they rode to church on the church bus. Reverend Bill took a big panel truck to Louisville and got fifty boxes of clothes to sell. When he brought them back to the store, the girls helped him unload the truck and opened the boxes.

Pastor Pascal

Reverend Jasper was a good man, and a good pastor. However, some pastors did not manage to always practice what they preached.

In Kentucky's Appalachian Mountains a one room school became vacant due to redistricting. A group of believers decided to investigate about using the building for a church. They went to the local Board of Education to get permission to use it.

After meeting and worshipping for a short time, the congregation talked about purchasing the lot and building. They contacted the school board again and learned that the price was $500. Several people donated money according to their personal finances. After a few weeks of collecting money, the offerings accumulated enough to make the purchase.

The pastor, George Pascal, was commissioned to make the transaction. When he returned to church the next Sunday, he told the people that the property belonged to them. Everyone rejoiced to have a local church home. However, Pastor Pascal didn't show them the deed. One church member, Cora Allen, wondered why he didn't produce the deed for everyone to see.

She continued feeling as if something was not correct about it all. She contacted the treasurer, Mollie Eversole about her concerns. Cora queried, "Wonder why Brother Pascal didn't pass the deed around for us to see?"

Millie answered "What are you getting at?"

Cora said "Just feel something queer about it, that's all."

An affronted Millie raged, "Don't you start something, Cora Allen. Don't you speak to me again if you're saying Brother Pascal has cheated us some way. Just leave now and don't come back if that's what you're trying to stir up."

Cora left and went home. Early the next morning she bathed, washed her hair, arranged it, and got dressed with special care. She drove to the local courthouse and asked to see the deed. After viewing it a few minutes, she asked for a copy of the document. The court clerk printed a copy and gave it to her.

Her first stop was Millie's house. Millie was sitting on her front porch in a hickory-barked straight-backed chair. Its mate was leaning against the wall so dogs wouldn't get in it and ruin the chair bottoms when they scratched.

Cora said, "Well, Millie, I have something for you to see."

Millie rose to her feet and said, "I told you not to speak to me again, if it's still the same lies on Brother Pascal."

Cora said, "Come here and see the proof for yourself. See if I'm not right."

Millie's husband charged out the front door to the porch and grabbed the copy of the deed and spit ambeer over the porch hand rail. Then he looked at the copy of the deed. "Dad-blame it, Millie, she's right. Come and see this yourself. Of all the meanness I've ever seen. He's robbed us!"

When Millie looked at the deed she had to sit down in the chair quickly. "Lord, have mercy. Cora you are right. Sorry I talked to you so mean. We have to go show this to the other church members. Why did Pastor Pascal do this to us: only sign his name on the ownership line. It's legally his!"

When the others saw the deed, they disbanded and went to other churches. Pastor Pascal retained ownership of the property. At his death, his children sold it and divided the money. His three daughters all had women for mates. His son married a woman and moved to Hamilton, Ohio. His wife came home early and caught him in bed with another man.

* * * *

The next few days, the girls were busy unpacking, folding, sorting, and hanging the clothes. They made sure each item was priced and sorted by size.

The girls had a pay phone installed on the store porch. Cora had the electric company come and turn the electricity back on to the store. They had a pop machine installed, too. They made money from both of these machines. The profits from these two alone paid the electric bill on the house and the store.

The opening day soon arrived. The store was crowded with people. Some were lookers, but most of them were buying clothing for themselves or their families. The girls had to continue opening boxes of clothing and putting them out to sell. Each girl worked in the store every day except Sunday when they went to church. When only a few unopened boxes remained, Pastor Bill went to Louisville and brought back another load. They gave Brother Bill half of the money each week to be used for the church's expenses.

The girls bought candy bars by the box and doubled the price when they were sold. They bought underwear from dollar stores and doubled the price of them, too. Some other items they sold were aspirin, coffee, gum, and cigarettes. No sales tax had to be paid on the used clothing. They did however have to pay taxes on the pop, candy, or any other special items that they sold.

If they wanted some of the clothes for themselves, they had to pay for them just like the customers did. As promised, each girl paid five dollars a week from their individual wages to Brother Bill in exchange for the furniture he had provided. Their last purchase was a sofa that let out into a bed. The bed was used only when a relative or a boyfriend stayed the night. Boyfriends only came on Saturday night. No one was allowed to live there with the four girls.

Cora said, "Girls, it's time for us to buy coal. We can get six tons for $120. Each of us can pay one fourth of it. Oh I know! My brother Jimmy hauls coal; we can get him to deliver it for us. "

Nancy Maggard and the Veteran

In fact, Jimmy delivered coal for a lot of people in the community.

Willard Moore was a wheelchair-bound Vietnam veteran who lived in Appalachia. He drew a disability check from the military. He owned a big house with a coal furnace for heat in the winter. He also owned a farm with rich soil. Part of it was located between a river and the railroad tracks. Every year he bought coal from the same man, Jimmy Allen. Willard asked Jimmy to bring him a load of coal for his furnace.

When Jimmy got there, Willard said, "I guess this will be my last load of coal. I plan to go to a veterans' home in Louisville and stay until I die."

Jimmy answered, "Why do you want to leave this beautiful house and farm?"

Willard said, "I can't take care of myself and tend my furnace. I have to hire a schoolboy to come by and take the ashes out and put more coal in the furnace. I'm so afraid that it's not done right and the house will catch on fire. Each day I have to maneuver my wheelchair outside and be sure everything is done correctly so I can have some peace."

Jimmy said, "Why don't you hire someone to stay here to take care of you? That way you can stay home."

Willard replied, "Who on Earth could I get? I don't have any *idee* who I could get."

Jimmy answered, "Get some woman that would like to have a good home and living provided for her."

"Do you think anyone would really want to take all this on?" Willard asked.

"Offhand, how about Nancy Maggard? She's a strong hardworking woman with three young'uns. She'd probably like to have a home for herself and her kids." Jimmy proposed.

Willard said, "Maybe you could ask her. If she agrees, we might try it for a week to see how it works."

Jimmy said, "I will, but you know she'd have to bring her kids with her. She'd have to take trips into town at night for 'social visits' if you know what I mean..."

Willard answered, "That's okay by me; I can't be a real husband because of my injuries. We'd have to legally marry if she continues to stay here though, and of course her young'uns are welcome."

Jimmy said, "I'll go ask her as soon as this coal is unloaded into your basement."

He went outside and opened the little metal door on the house's coal chute. He backed the truck up to the side of the house and let down the tailgate. He shoveled the coal out and tossed it down the chute. When he was finished he went to Nancy

Maggard's parents' house to speak to her. When Jimmy got to the Maggards' house, Nancy opened the door.

"Howdy, Jimmy, what brings you out this way?" Nancy asked.

"Howdy, Nancy, how's it going here living with your mom and dad?" Jimmy asked.

"It's getting crowded in this little house with my three young'uns and my check doesn't go very far," Nancy answered.

"You know Willard Moore? Well he's got a problem being disabled and all. He needs someone to move in with him to help or he'll have to leave here and move to the old soldiers' home in Louisville," Jimmy said.

"That's too bad. I really feel sorry for him." Nancy responded.

Jimmy continued, "You need to go over there and talk to him and see if you'd be interested in staying with him. He said you could stay a week to see if you both are interested in the arrangement. He also said you could bring the young'uns."

Nancy blinked in disbelief, "I've been worried how I could make a good life for my kids. This sounds like an answer to my prayers. I'll go. Help me pack up our few belongings right now."

Nancy, Jimmy, and the two older children stacked their meager things in cardboard boxes and loaded them in the bed of his coal truck. Then Nancy and Jimmy crowded themselves and the children into the cab of the truck and rode over to Willard's large white house.

Upon arrival, Jimmy helped Nancy and her three children out of the truck cab. They walked up on the front porch and Jimmy knocked on the door. While they stood there they saw a porch swing on one end of the porch, and three hickory-bottomed straight-back chairs leaning against the wall of the house. Behind the swing a wisteria vine grew. The vine was attached to the underside edge at the top of the porch which made it form a leafy shady backdrop for the swing. Dangling from the vine were numerous large grape like clusters of purple flowers that gave off a pleasant sweet smell.

Willard yelled, "Come in, it's open."

When they entered the house, Willard eyed the little group of visitors. He saw a red-haired sturdy-looking woman in her late twenties, a stocky black-haired boy that looked about ten, another younger boy with blonde hair that might be six, and a little blue-eyed red-haired girl that was probably four years old, and Jimmy.

"Howdy," Willard said as he continued looking at them.

"Howdy," chorused Nancy and the children. They saw a young black-haired man in a wheelchair. He looked to be in his late twenties, too. Jimmy stepped forward and shook Willard's hand.

"Well, here they are," Jimmy said, pointing to Nancy and the children.

"They are willing to stay a week and see if you all can make it permanent. Willard, do you promise to provide for them and be good to Nancy and her kids? Do you agree for her to go to town at night occasionally?"

Willard said, "I do promise."

Jimmy continued, "Nancy, do you promise to cook, clean, take care of Willard, raise a garden each summer, and can food."

Nancy stepped forward and said, "I do promise, and my young'uns will help me. I have trained them to work and they are well-behaved and mind." Nancy shook Willard's hand to seal the agreement. Jimmy and Nancy and the two boys went outside and carried in the boxes of belongings.

Willard said, "You all can take the whole upstairs to live in. I have a room down here that I sleep in."

The little boys, Nancy, and Jimmy carried the boxes upstairs, and saw four bedrooms and two bathrooms. Each child and Nancy had their own bedroom, and the boys had one bathroom while Nancy and the little girl, Sally, would share the other one. When they went back downstairs, Sally was sitting in Willards' lap, talking like they were old friends.

Nancy said, "That's Sally, my big boy is Ricky, and this boy", pointing to her youngest son, "is Johnny".

Willard said, "Good to meet y'all. Are you hungry?"

The children chorused, "Yes!"

Nancy went into the kitchen and searched through the pantry shelves and refrigerator. She pulled out pork tenderloin and started frying some of it in a black cast iron skillet. She opened cans of corn and green beans that she put in enamelware kettles to cook.

Ricky and Johnny peeled potatoes for Nancy which she cut into cubes and put in a large kettle of water to boil and mash. Then she mixed cornmeal, eggs, baking powder, soda, melted lard, and milk in a large mixing bowl. Lastly she poured the mixture into another large cast iron skillet. She put it in the oven to bake. The boys washed the large oak table and set it with plates, glasses and silverware.

While supper was cooking, Jimmy, Willard, and Sally were in the living room talking. They were amused by Sally's chatter.

When everything was done, Nancy had the children wash their hands and call everyone to eat. The food smelled and tasted delicious. All of them were hungry so they ate heartily. Nancy proved herself to be a good cook. After supper the children carried the dishes and the silverware to the kitchen sink. Ricky washed while Johnny rinsed them and put everything in a draining rack to dry.

Jimmy said, "Well, I'll see you all in a week to find out the verdict. If you need to go back home, I'll move you."

"Thank you, Jimmy, I appreciate your help," replied Nancy.

"Glad to oblige", he answered as he headed for the door to leave.

Nancy said to Willard, "Do you need anything before we go upstairs to unpack?"

"No, I'm okay," Willard said.

Nancy and the children went upstairs to unpack, but they saved the boxes in case they would be needed at the end of the week. The children ran from room to room exploring.

Ricky said excitedly, "Look how many bedrooms! I won't have to sleep on a couch!"

Johnny squealed, "This one's mine!"

Nancy said, "We'll have lots of room. We can all spread out up here."

The bedrooms were painted white and each one was a corner room with a window on each outside wall. In each bedroom there was an iron and brass double bed with coil springs and a soft mattress. The beds had clean sheets, pillows, hand sewn quilts and pretty bedspreads. Each bedroom also had an oak chest of drawers and a dresser in which to store their folded belongings and personal items. There was a large mirror over the dresser. There also was a closet for hanging clothes in each room. It didn't take long for them to unpack their few possessions.

The bathrooms and halls were in the middle of the house. They were painted apple green with white fixtures. All the floors had tongue-and-groove wood sealed with shellac. As Nancy and the boys started towards the stairs, Ricky said "Mommy, we all had to stay in the same room at Granny and Pa's; this is like living in a palace. Here we have our own room, and that was a mighty good supper. It beats even a Sunday dinner at Pa's and Granny's."

Johnny said, "I like it here, too. Mr. Moore seems nice. I liked the supper tonight too. I hope we can stay."

Then they went back downstairs to be with Willard. They needed to visit and talk to get to know each other. They walked into the white living room and sat on the couch and side chairs. They were soft and covered with a pretty print blue fabric with small green swirling leaves on them. The room itself was large and had two windows that had white pulled-back drapes on them that let in a lot of light. Willard closed the drapes at night and in the winter to keep out the cold. There were three more rooms on the first floor. There was a kitchen with an electric stove, cabinets, a large table with six chairs, and a sink that was fully plumbed. There was a bathroom painted blue with white fixtures and a large shower. The other room was Willard's white bedroom. The furniture was similar to the upstairs.

Nancy said, "Well, Willard, we all like your house, and if you are good to us and provide for us, we will stay."

Willard answered, "I'm easygoing. If you all clean and cook like you did this evening, I think it will work out. Each day coal has to be put in the furnace, the ashes have to be taken out, and dumped on the ash pile in the back yard. I'll need someone to help me get into the seat in the shower to bathe and help me out so I won't fall. I have a plastic urinal that I use at night so I don't have to get up to use the bathroom. Each morning I empty it in the commode."

Nancy said, "Me and the young'uns can do all that. I see you have a wringer washing machine on one side of the kitchen and two rinse tubs on a frame with legs. Washing clothes will be much easier here than what we've been used to."

Nancy continued, "Kids, it's time to go to bed so we can get up early and get you all on the school bus. Since we're over here, we'll have to go to a different school. I'll get out the paperwork tonight to give to the teachers. Willard, do you need anything before we go upstairs for the night?"

"No, I'm fine. I'll see you all in the morning." Willard answered.

Early the next morning, Nancy rose and cooked breakfast for everyone and saw the two older children off to school on the bus and started Sally playing with her dolls. Then she washed the dishes, swept, and mopped the kitchen floor. Next she took ashes out of the coal furnace and dumped them on the ash pile at the back of the house. Afterward Nancy put coal in the furnace to keep the house warm. Then Nancy started working by straightening and cleaning the upstairs. After the beds were made, she dusted and oiled the furniture with O-Cedar oil. Next Nancy mopped the upstairs floors and bleached the bathroom fixtures. As she went down the stairs, they got mopped, too.

Sally climbed in Willard's lap and said, "Tell me a story. I like stories."

Willard smiled and said, "Let me think a minute. I'll tell you the Three Little Pigs story. "As he told the story he added sound effects and funny voices for the characters, making Sally giggle.

Now it was time to start cooking dinner, with enough left over for supper. Nancy got potatoes out of the potato bin in the basement. She peeled and cooked them in chunks to cook with a side of spare ribs. Next she opened cans of sauerkraut and green beans which she put in enamel pans to heat. Nancy made biscuits and saved some extra dough to make a peach cobbler. When everything was ready, Sally, Willard, and she sat down to eat dinner. Since Nancy was tired she didn't talk much.

Willard said, "You are a good cook and worker, Nancy."

She answered, "Thank you. I want to get everything organized and cleaned today. Then it will be easier to keep everything neat."

Willard continued, "You know, we will have to marry if you keep staying here but I can never be a husband to you. If you need other men in your life, I will understand."

Nancy replied, "I don't mind hard work. Things are much easier in this house than at Pa and Ma's. I'll probably go up to town next weekend and see some of my friends. I'll get things ready for you all before I leave."

Willard said, "I appreciate that. I can do a few things for myself, and the boys can help a lot. We'll manage."

After dinner, Nancy laid Sally down for a nap and washed the dishes and started cleaning the downstairs. She stripped the sheets from Willard's bed and collected the towels from his bathroom. She put them in the washing machine, washed, and dried them on the outside clothesline. She put clean linens on his bed and clean towels in his bathroom. Next she dusted, swept, and mopped the other rooms. Nancy started putting things away in closets, dressers, and cabinets. As Nancy worked she made sure everything was organized so housekeeping would be easier.

The household settled down into a comfortable routine. Everyone worked hard and the two older children went to school. Little Sally stayed home and developed a strong connection with Willard. She fetched his pipe, water, and anything else he needed. Willard told and read many stories to her.

At the end of the week, Willard and Nancy got married at the county courthouse with the children in attendance. The children beamed at the long awaited chance to have a father figure in their lives. The older boys had endured many bad comments from other children and some unfeeling adults. Some had called them bastards and poor white trash living on welfare. The children were happy to call Willard daddy.

As time went on Nancy took occasional trips to bars at the county seat. There she met some of her friends and other men.

Sometimes she stayed out all night with them, but she planned her trysts over the weekend when her children wouldn't miss school. The children learned to cook simple staple foods while she was away. They also took care of the household chores. The boys helped bathe Willard and see that he was well taken care of.

Willard drew a pension of about $5,000 that helped raise the growing family. The children and Nancy grew a large garden and canned it each year to help provide for them. Willard bought a hog every month or two and had it butchered for meat for the family. Over the years, Nancy had seven more pregnancies that were surnamed Moore. The children loved Willard and he loved them very much. It was a happy home. They all graduated high school and did well in life. The children eventually moved to Indiana to be near relatives, and one boy became a preacher.

When Willard died, Nancy sold the house and farm and bought a house in Indiana to be near her children. She lived there until she died at 80 years of age.

* * * *

The girls bought the six tons of coal and each paid their part. Lizzie bought a TV that they all watched. They also had a record player and records. The girls bought pretty clothes for themselves at a thrift shop in town and from their own stock of donated clothes. The girls went to the nearest town every other week and bought $80 worth of groceries for which they split the bill four ways. They bought mainly staples to cook for the next two weeks. Some things they bought to cook were soup beans, kraut, wieners, chow-chow, and blackberries to eat with dumplings.

The girls worked each day at the store, but they closed for dinner. They usually cooked soup and ate it with crackers. It was also closed all day on Sunday for church attendance.

At one special church service, Cora's mother was in attendance. Brother Bill said to Cora's mother Bertha, "You should be very proud of your girl and her friends. All of them sing at church each service. They are some of the prettiest and most talented girls anywhere in the country."

Not only did the girls sing at church, but before long the girls formed a band, too. They dressed in bright neon-colored wigs and named themselves funny names. Two boys played guitars, and one was the announcer for the group. They did comedy routines and sang mostly country music and gospel songs, performing at schools and auditoriums. One of their favorite songs was "The New River Train". They gave half the money earned to the Board of Education of the county in which they performed. It was used to buy things all the schools needed, like a new roof, books, furniture, or whatever was the county's greatest need. They charged $2.50 for adults and 50¢ for child admission each night. They travelled in a van to each performance. Their half of the money was split six ways.

The girls took part in the church's program at Christmas. They sang and played characters in a nativity scene that featured a real baby for Jesus. The church gave out baskets of fruit and nuts to needy people, and the girls got a large basket filled with candy, nuts, oranges, apples, grapes, and bananas as a Christmas gift.

They continued running the store for about two years. They helped the Metcalfs get in coal and wood, wash clothes, mow the lawn, tend the garden, and can food.

The Rape

The girls were lucky to live somewhere safe; they didn't have to worry about strangers when they were outside alone on the Metcalfs' farm. Although it was a rare occurrence in the mountains to be molested by a stranger, it happened to one of Cora's sisters.

One afternoon as the Allen family sat on the porch threading whole green beans onto long pieces of thread to hang up to dry, their mother Bertha said, "Della, we've only got enough beans to finish out today. Get that five gallon bucket and fill it with beans for us to thread tomorrow."

Every year they dried whole bean pods to eat in the winter. Drying beans was a cheap way to preserve them. Many times they might not have money to buy Mason jars or lids. When the beans were to be eaten, they were cooked in a kettle of water. The hot water softened the beans to make them edible.

Fourteen-year-old Della got the bucket and walked down the holler to the corn patch where the flat type of stick beans grew on vines, clinging to cornstalks or poles for support. Also in the corn patch were planted cornfield pumpkins which grew to be large tough shelled, light yellowish orange. They were usually cut with an axe or by a strong person with a sharp knife.

The pumpkin vines covered the open area between the corn rows. The Allens also planted cushaws, or large crook-necked squash, in the corn patch. They grew on long vines on the ground like the pumpkins. When the cushaws were ripe, their necks were green and white striped. The family used the pumpkins and cushaws to make pies or feed animals. Their meat could be canned, dried, or frozen for future use. Sometimes the women would cut the pumpkins into small pieces, boil them, and then fry the boiled chunks with hog lard in a cast iron skillet. They added spices and sugar to enhance the taste and the mixture turned out to be delicious.

As Della walked through the corn rows, she stepped carefully around the vines of the pumpkins and squash. She had to watch out for stinging worms on the cornstalks. They were called "packsaddles" and really hurt if you got stung. She hurriedly picked the long flat Kentucky Wonder beans from the vines. Since they were large, it didn't take long for her to fill the bucket. She sat the bucket down and pushed them deeper into the bucket to make room for more.

Just as she had finished her task, a strange man stepped out from behind the corn rows. He had a pistol and pointed it at her.

Della gasped in shock, "Who are you, and where did you come from?"

The stranger said, "Never mind. Take off your clothes and lay down or I'll shoot you. I mean it."

Della believed the man would really shoot her so she obeyed. The man raped her and jumped up and ran off through the corn patch toward the mouth of the holler. Della was crying and fumbled around for her clothes. Trembling, she got dressed, got the bucket of beans, and walked towards the family's house. When she got to the house, she sat the bucket down on the porch and went to the outside toilet. She was bleeding from being raped. She yelled for her older sister Vivian to come to the toilet. She told Vivian what had happened and asked her to bring her some clean underpants.

Vivian said, "Whatever you do, you can't tell Ma and Pa what happened. You know how they are. They'll say you made plans to meet that man down there. They'll call you a whore and throw it up to you every chance they get. You must not tell them about this!"

Della sobbed, "I know how they are. It's bad that I can't tell them and I have to suffer through this experience without their help."

Vivian got Della a new pair of clean underpants and clean rags to stuff inside them. She was careful not to let anyone see her collect these things. She took them back to Della and waited until she had time to get dressed, and they walked back to the house together.

By this time, the other family members were inside the house. The girls sat outside on the porch until bedtime, and they went inside to go to sleep.

As time went on, Della missed her period for two months. She was in a panic when she told told Vivian about it, "Vivian, I think I'm pregnant! I don't know what I'll do. They'll turn me out of our house. I can't provide for a baby and myself."

Vivian said, "You must go up to Cincinnati and stay with our brother Lloyd. You can keep house and babysit for them. His wife Clara wants to go back to work. She'll pay you five dollars a week."

After contacting Lloyd and letting him know that she was coming on Tuesday at noon, Della packed and boarded a bus to Cincinnati. Lloyd, Clara, and their three children came to pick her up at the bus station. Della was very busy doing daily chores of cooking, cleaning, and child care. Clara went to work as a cashier at a nearby food market, and she did pay Della the five dollars a week as promised.

As time went on, Della started showing that she was pregnant. She wore a tight band around her belly, but she still showed.

Lloyd said, "Della, I know you're pregnant, and I can't have you stay up here like that. The neighbors will talk and I can't have that happen."

Della cried, "I can't and I won't go home! I'll go to the Ohio River and jump in before I'll do that! You know how Ma and Pa are, I'll never have a minute's peace. I was raped by a stranger in the corn patch and I couldn't help myself. Now I'm pregnant!"

Lloyd and Clara saw that Della was really determined to kill herself before she would go home. They also knew how Bertha and Charles would treat her, so they decided to tell a lie. They told the Ohio folks that Della was married and that her husband was killed in a car wreck. They told the family back home that Della had gotten married in Ohio and that her husband had died in a car wreck.

Della continued to stay with Lloyd and Clara. She named her baby Jonas. When he was about one-year-old, she met a friend of Lloyd's and got married. He helped her raise Jonas, and they had four more children together. They had a happy life.

* * * *

The whole community was benefitted by the store. Alas, rumors were spreading about a new dam that was going to be built. The water would cover their house and store. They soon learned that it was true and the time was quickly approaching. The girls started selling off the contents of the store. As time went by, they didn't purchase any new merchandise. The dam was built and the water was slowly rising. In a few months, all of the area where they lived and worked would be covered with water. The girls parceled out their furniture to put in each of their new homes. Cora had her items sent to her parents' house.

One of Cora's brothers wanted to marry Jeanie. His wife had run away with another man. He was working in Chicago and wanted her to go there to live with him. She refused to marry him. She didn't want to live in a city. Jeanie loved the mountains and didn't want to leave. Later she married a local boy and moved to the next county, where he worked in the mines and she got work in a clothing store.

It was sad when each of the girls got married and moved away. One by one they left Cora. Sue married a young man from their band and they made their home on a small farm where they raised tobacco and hogs to sell. They continued singing and playing music for extra money.

Lizzie married an older man that she met in the store. He was retired from the army and drew a check each month. He did carpenter work and he treated her well. They had five children over a period of several years.

Cora packed a suitcase and moved to Chicago to live with her brother Sam and his city wife. She got a job working in a factory. Cora was thrifty and saved her money, because she was determined to be able to take care of herself.

The Prisoner
and the Taxi Driver

There was another girl who shared this determination to take care of herself and her family.

Ellen Trosper lived across the hill from Cora Allen's family. She was in her late teens and slightly mentally challenged, but she was a good worker in the house. Ellen cooked, did dishes, and swept and mopped the floors. Her parents were Pete and Jenny Trosper. Pete and Jenny were both disabled and they drew pension checks each month and received commodity food items as well. Pete had clubbed feet and walked on the sides of them. Jenny had a peg leg and sat in a recliner a lot each day. While she sat there, she made herself useful by sewing beautiful quilts. They took a homeless mentally challenged boy named Bill into their household. He helped with milking the cows, gardening and any other farm work.

The family lived in a three room shotgun house. It had a kitchen, a sitting room, and one bedroom with two beds. Ellen slept in one, and her parents slept in the other while Bill slept on the couch in the front room. The kitchen had a stove which burned wood or coal for cooking their meals and for heat in the winter. There was one kitchen table with six chairs, a meal chest that held flour and meal, and a large three-cornered cupboard in the room. They had a sink with pipes to bring in the water, with a pitcher hand pump and a drain pipe that let the water out.

With no electricity, they lit coal oil lamps at night to see, read, work, play games, or just talk together. The family also had a small log house that they used as a wash house. It was floored and had large clay-chinked log walls. They had a washing machine that was powered by a gasoline motor and a stove in the washhouse that was used to heat the water and for warmth. Cold water was heated in large tubs and poured into the washer to clean their clothes.

Their shotgun house had a picket fence around the yard with climbing rose bushes adorning it. The yard was abuzz with bees pollinating all the flowers that grew in it. Bill also spent time working in the yard and tending flowers. The family went to the grocery store in a horse drawn jolt wagon. Along the way they picked up coal which had fallen from the coal trucks. They filled the sacks with coal for heating and cooking. When Ellen was eighteen, she married a seventy-year-old man named Jeff, who had been in trouble most of his life. He had even spent time in prison. Ellen didn't know much about him when they married. She just wanted to get married and have her own home.

In the summer, she and her husband sat on the front porch on benches and listened to records on their wind-up record player. They lived in a small shack of a house; living was very hard. They had to rely on commodity foods. Sometimes, they got meal, flour, peanut butter, and any other food that was given that month.

Because Jeff hadn't worked much in his younger life, he didn't draw Social Security. They did however get a little welfare check. Jeff could cook, and sometimes he helped Ellen with the meals. Many times there was little to eat. Sometimes they only had gravy and bread, or beans and potatoes from their small garden, to feed them and their three boys that were born about a year apart.

In winter when the boys were little, they didn't have shoes. She had them wear three pairs of socks for warmth. Most of the family's clothes came from local churches and secondhand stores. When the children got old enough to go to school, Ellen walked them out of the mouth of the holler to catch the school bus each day.

After a few years of enduring such a hard life, Ellen got a job at a restaurant washing the dishes and helping to cook. She used her wages to buy milk and groceries for the family. Ellen bathed the boys in a bathtub each night. It had a drain pipe, but had to be filled with buckets of water. After the bath each night, Ellen had the boys put on pajamas and helped them with their lessons before she put them all in the second bed in the house.

As time went on Ellen developed a romantic relationship with a regular customer of the restaurant named Joe. He was a taxi driver and a veteran and received a retirement pension. One day, Joe came and picked up Ellen and the three boys with their luggage and moved them to his house in another community. Ellen had to enroll the boys in a different school. She got a job working in a restaurant in that town. She still washed dishes and helped the cook, but sometimes she was allowed to cook some meals herself.

After she lived with Joe two or three weeks, Jeff showed up to get Ellen and his three children.

Jeff announced, "I want you to make my family come home. They belong to me."

Joe answered, "Do you see chains or locks around their necks?"

Jeff said, "No I don't, but they will leave if you tell them to."

"They are free to leave if they want to," responded Joe.

None of the boys or Ellen stood up to leave with Jeff. He stood there staring at them for a few seconds before he turned around and stomped out of the house.

That night Jeff had a heart attack and died. A daughter from Louisville by his first marriage came and paid for his funeral and burial. Shortly afterwards, Joe and Ellen got married, got a U-Haul and moved to Indiana. They both got jobs there and finished raising the boys. After the boys grew up, they had families of their own, and continued living in Indiana.

* * * *

Cora bought a house with a large parcel of land at the head of a holler back in her native county. She continued working in Chicago and saving to buy all new furniture for her house. Cora took night classes to become a practical nurse. Her plan was to move back to Kentucky and work as a nurse. After the training was finished, she quit her job and moved home to the mountains. After arriving, she went to a local store and purchased furniture for the whole house. The store owner was so overjoyed by the big sale that he had the furniture delivered and set up the same day.

Cora had to walk out of the holler and catch a bus to get to her practical nurse position each day. She had many patients before she married at age twenty-two. She met her husband, Tommy Moore, in town. Eventually, she would have three children, the first of which was born when Cora was twenty-three.

Tommy had no car or job, and came from a poor family. He had nothing besides the shirt on his back, but he had the gift of gab and levity. He had many jobs over the years and did some mining. He started working in the "Happy Pappy" program in the 1960s. It was employment for miners without jobs, and it was created during the Democratic War on Poverty. He received $275 a month, and his work consisted of cleaning up brush around river beds or other areas. Sometimes he swept in and around the local courthouse. It was temporary work, and made up jobs or busy work.

One of Tommy's passions was squirrel hunting. He was a good shot with a rifle. From the beginning of squirrel hunting season, he was out in the woods most of his spare time. He had to quietly sneak into the woods near walnut or hickory nut trees, and look for signs of nut shells on the ground. Then he hid and waited for a squirrel to come out to eat.

There were many wooded areas where they lived and the forest teemed with squirrels and nut trees. When he killed one, he skinned and gutted it in the field. When he took it home, he cut it up in pieces. Tommy and Cora did not leave any of the squirrel's meat to waste. Tommy used an axe to open the skull and extract the brain. Cora fried the rinsed and salted brain in pieces of hog lard in a cast iron skillet. When it was cooked, the squirrel tasted delicious.

Later on Tommy was hired to drive coal trucks and haul the freight to railyards to be loaded onto trains. He was well paid and provided for his three children when he had this job.

Everything went well for Cora and Tommy until he reached forty-nine years old in their fifteenth year of marriage. One night he didn't come home. Cora was very worried, paced the floor, cried and prayed all night. The next day, she found out that he had run off with a twenty-two-year-old cousin of Cora's named Emma. Cora was devastated. Soon, Tommy and Cora got a divorce.

The divorce cost Cora quite a bit of money that she had to pay to Tommy. The money came from the strip mine that was on the land that she had bought before their marriage. He went to live with Emma's parents and started building a house on his uncle's land without a deed to the property. He also built a smokehouse, chicken house, crib, and barn. He paid $25 a month for rent on the land. He also helped clear the land.

For six months, Tommy tried to take the children away from Cora, but the judge didn't give him custody. He never bought them a Christmas present after that nor did he pay any child support. They had to go on welfare and SSI to survive.

One cold winter day, Cora's three-year-old Timmy got very sick. She expected that he had pneumonia. She made a poultice out of cooked white onions and laid on his chest to try to break up the congestion. She called Tommy. He cussed her out and hung up on her without finding out that Timmy was sick. Then she called her former mother-in-law, June, to tell her about Timmy's illness. She recognized Cora's voice and hung up, too.

Since Timmy didn't have any shoes, Cora put four pairs of socks on his feet, extra clothes, and a hand-me-down coat on him. She dressed herself in her warmest clothes and coat. She called her mother to come to her house to take care of her other two children.

Next she put Timmy on her back, packed him out of the holler, and flagged down a car to take her to town. She took him to the hospital and stayed three days with him. She slept in a chair with her head lying on Timmy's bed.

Tommy and his mother came to the hospital crying and acting so concerned. Cora picked up a metal folding chair and yelled, "Get out of here right now or I'm going to hit you with this chair!"

Believing that Cora was actually going to swing the chair and hit them, they quickly exited the room.

The Miner and Bootlegger

If a woman found herself in a dangerous or unproductive relationship with a man in this time, she would often have to take drastic measures to protect herself.

Patrick Russell was a union foreman in a mine in Appalachia. He was large and mean, with a low boiling point. The miners knew not to cause him any trouble. He took care of his problems with his fist and his pistol. Several miners had witnessed and experienced his wrath. If there was a strike in the mine, Patrick took his pistol and helped guard the mine entrance. If a worker came that wanted to work, he beat him up or shot him. It was known that he had killed some miners but was not prosecuted because people were afraid of him. Patrick also owned a saloon, and made moonshine to sell in the saloon and to transport to other restaurants as well as individuals. His saloon was a rowdy place with prostitutes and much violence.

His wife, Lula, was a defeated, gentle woman. She had two sons, David who was six, and Larry who was eight. One day when Patrick was driving drunk with his family as passengers, he wrecked on the sharp curb and hit the side of the mountain. Lula was killed. The rest of them were bruised and scratched from the shattered glass and the impact of the wreck.

After the funeral, Patrick's mother, Polly, moved in with him to help with housework and took care of the boys while Patrick worked in the mine and the saloon. A few months later, forty-year-old Patrick met a sixteen-year-old girl named Sheila. She was from a poor mountain family, and was dazzled by the money he lavished on her. Soon she agreed to marry him, and Patrick's mother moved back to her house. Sheila and Patrick had a stormy marriage. She had many black eyes and bruises, but she was used to be being beaten by her parents and believed it was normal behavior.

As time went by, she had two daughters named Susan and Iris. When they were four and three, Patrick got into a disagreement with the deputy sheriff and shot and wounded him. The county had a new prosecuting attorney that was trying to make a name for himself by prosecuting lawbreakers.

The new prosecuting attorney had him arrested, and when he got out on bail Patrick came home drunk and upset. He took his temper out on Sheila and started beating her. When she tried to defend herself, the violence escalated, and he threatened to kill her and started choking her. She managed to get free and escape. As she ran outside, Patrick grabbed his pistol and chased her. Since he was drunk and it was dark, his aim was hindered.

Sheila just barely escaped with her life. She knew enough about Patrick to never go back to him; she knew he would kill her. Shaken with fright, she ran up into the mountain to a friend's house where she borrowed some clothes and some money. She begged her friend to drive her to town so she could catch the midnight bus to Michigan. Sheila had some relatives there that would give her a place to live until she could get a job to support herself. She told her friend that Patrick would kill her if he found her, and that she must leave to save her own life. She had no choice but to leave her girls.

Patrick was given a ten-year prison sentence for shooting the deputy. His mother Polly came back to take care of the children. By this time, the two boys were older and could take care of themselves and help her with the work in the house yard and garden. Since she was getting older and did not have the money to take care of the little girls, Polly took Susan and Iris to an orphanage in a nearby county where they stayed for five years.

When Sheila's dad started drawing a black lung check, he and his wife learned that an interested party was about to adopt Susan and Iris. Her parents went to the orphanage and took them back to their home to keep. Meanwhile, Sheila lived in Michigan and she got a divorce from Patrick. About once every two months, she came to visit her girls and her parents. The girls had a good life with their grandparents. They were given lots of love and they got to see their half-brothers often.

When she got older, Iris moved to Michigan to live with her mother. She stayed in Michigan and married a man local to the area. In her later years she developed dementia and died.

One night, Sheila met a soldier named Gary Winsted in a bar and struck up a relationship with him, and months later they married. He was a career soldier and in later life, Sheila collected a large sum of money because of an insurance claim filed during his service. Sheila had a good life with Gary.

Susan first moved to Nashville to live with some cousins. She got a job working for a country music star. She was a lively redhead who loved people and dancing; she sometimes clogged on the Opry when needed. Susan later moved to Michigan where some of her other cousins lived. She had one daughter. Susan was involved in an automobile accident, sued the state for damages, and received a large sum of money.

Patrick got out of prison and went back to his bar. Before long he was involved in more criminal activity and went back to prison. Once he got out again, he continued a life of drinking and fighting with every woman that he lived with. He had become an alcoholic. His sons were grown and had each joined the military. They both became good husbands and fathers. One of them stayed in the military until he retired.

* * * *

Once Timmy was healthy enough to leave the hospital, a neighbor came to the hospital and gave Cora and Timmy a ride as far as the car could go. Then, Cora packed Timmy on her back the rest of the way up the holler to her house. She used a teakettle of hot water with Vick's Salve to help keep Timmy's airways open. Cora had him hold his head over the water, take deep breaths to help him breath better, and he soon recovered.

As time went on, with Tommy's drinking and getting sick with cancer, he couldn't pay the $25 land rent. His uncle made him move out and took his house and buildings. Then, Emma left him and got another man. Tommy came back to Cora and wanted her to take care of him, but Cora became irate and chased him out of the house.

Later on Cora met another man and fell in love with him. His name was Louie Johnson. She didn't know him as well as she thought. After marriage, Louie's major flaw surfaced. He was a heavy drinker, but he was good to her. One night he didn't come home and she grieved all night again.

She cried aloud, "Is this going to be a rerun of my first marriage? Why me, Lord? What's wrong with me? Am I just picking out the wrong kind of man?"

The next day she learned that he had wrecked their car and killed himself. The sheriff found two jars of moonshine in the car that survived the wreck. Cora buried him in their family's graveyard and never considered marriage again. She concentrated on her family, her church work, and singing. She had continued singing since her youth and enjoyed attending gospel singings.

The Haunted Barn

C ora Allen had friends that lived on a farm in another county. They were Ella and Ben Whitley. The Whitleys called her to come to their county seat for gospel singings and to go home with them for the night.

The gospel singing was very inspirational. Because there were five different singing groups it was late when it ended. Cora drove her car and followed them out to their farm. They ate a late snack of chocolate pie and milk before going to bed.

As they sat there eating, Ben said, "I want to tell you about the piano music."

Cora asked, "What piano music?"

Ben continued, "Every night, a ghost plays the old piano that's been left in the barn loft. That's why we were able to buy this farm for only $500."

Cora stuttered, "Ghost? $500?"

Ella interrupted, "Yes, the people that lived on this farm sold it to us because of the ghost. They were scared and just wanted to get away from here fast, so they let us have it for $500. We're ready to let it go for that, too. We thought the ghost would get tired after a while and stop, but we're tired from being kept awake every night."

Cora said, "When the music starts, I've got a flashlight and my pistol, and I'm not afraid of ghosts. If it starts playing, I'm going out there, but don't talk to me. I'll be operating in the spirit and talking to God."

They said good night to each other and went to bed. They had Cora sleep in a special bedroom that they saved only for company. At about midnight they were awakened by piano music coming from the barn. Cora jumped up, grabbed her flashlight and pistol and started walking towards the barn.

The Whitleys stood in the doorway watching as Cora neared the barn.

Ben yelled "Be careful! It might be dangerous!"

The piano sounds stopped and Cora turned around and went back to the house.

She said, "Please don't talk to me while I'm going after the ghost!"

They all went back to bed and tried to go to sleep. While they lay there, the piano noises started again. Cora jumped up, and grabbed her flashlight and gun again. As she headed for the door, Ben and Ella came out of their room to follow her. Cora went into the barn. Ben and Ella gradually walked towards the barn behind Cora.

Ben shouted, "Watch out! Be careful! It might be scary!"

The piano sounds stopped and Cora frowned as she stopped, too.

She said, "I've asked you to please be quiet. I'm never going to get to the bottom of this mystery if you talk or make noise. I'm talking to God in the spirit and you're interrupting it."

Ben said, "I'm sorry. This has got me so scared and confused. I promise I'll hush up if this starts again. "

They all went back to the house and went to bed. No sooner had they laid down, when the sounds started again. Cora jumped up and hurried out of the house towards the barn. As she got closer, she walked slowly and quietly. Ben and Ella walked toward her but were still lagging back out of fear. Neither of them spoke.

Cora went into the barn and sneaked up the ladder with the gun and flashlight in her pockets. She kept hearing the piano sounds. Cora inched over to the piano and shone the light on it. To her amazement the whole piano was swarming with rats. She grabbed her pistol and began shooting them. The live ones started scurrying away to hide.

Ben and Ella came running into barn screaming, "Cora, what's happened? Are you alright?"

Cora yelled back laughing, "I just killed the ghost AND the piano. It was just a swarm of rats. You need to buy a lot of rat bait and kill all of them before they take over the whole farm."

After they got back to the house, they sat around a kitchen table drinking coffee and laughing as they talked.

Cora asked, "Will you still sell me this farm for $500? If you are, I'll buy it."

Ben laughed, "Nooo way, since you killed our ghost."

* * * *

Cora's parents got older and moved in with *her*. Her father Charles still tried to boss everyone around. If Cora even mentioned another man he would exclaim, "We're not going to have a whorehouse around here!"

He questioned her every time she went someplace. Whatever she told him, he never believed her. Cora kept him for a few years until his death. Charles was buried beside his first wife and children at the cemetery where Cora attended church.

Later Cora found out that her mother, Bertha, had a will containing two tracts of land valued at about $300,000, made over to the wealthiest brother in the family. The land was rich in coal, and Cora and her siblings needed the money more. Cora had kept Bertha a number of years after her father's death and endured all her negative innuendos and insults. She thought Bertha should have left it to her or divided it evenly among her children.

Cora's daughter, Rachel, grew up to be a healthy strong woman. Because there were few opportunities for gainful employment in the area, she joined the military. After being on active duty for several years, she met a handsome young man, Luke Koger. They planned to get married one day in the future. Rachel and Luke started saving their money to buy a house. Months later they had enough for a down payment. Luke would live in the house, and both of them contribute to the house payment. Rachel would come home on furlough and join Luke for a few days when she could.

Since Cora had lost quite a bit of money when she got a divorce and because she didn't trust men when it came to money, Cora said several times, "Don't give money to a man you're not married to."

Rachel would always respond, "Mom, I trust him, and when I retire we'll have our house paid off. We'll be able to live on my pension and if he is retired, his pension too. We plan to marry when I get through with all my training to work with drug related military personnel. Since we won't have any big bills to pay, we can have a great life together."

This arrangement went on for a few years. One day Rachel decided to surprise Luke on an unexpected furlough. She drove about 150 miles from the base to Appalachia and their house. It was about 11 pm when she arrived. She was all excited and rushed into the house, and hurried into the bedroom to surprise him.

Rachel was the recipient of the surprise when she opened the bedroom door. She saw a startled disheveled Luke in the bed with another woman.

Rachel gasped, "What's she doing here!? How long has this been going on!? Who is she anyway!?"

Luke answered her questions with another question, "What are you doing here? Rachel, I'm going to marry her at the end of the month. She's Lola Casper from over on Ball Knob. I don't love you anymore. I've been trying to get up the courage to tell you. I didn't want to hurt you and lose the house payment. I couldn't swing it on my paycheck alone. We've been sleeping together for about the past four months."

Rachel stood there crying and gasping, "How could you do this to me? Am I just a paycheck?"

"No! No!" Luke answered, "I really did care for you once, but after I met Lola, I realized what a passionate love we have for each other. I never felt that with you. I'm really sorry."

Rachel said, "And to think of all the men I could have had that I turned down to be true to you! You will have to sell the house and give me half of the money."

Luke answered, "I won't sell the house. Me and Lola have to have a place to live, and besides, it's in my name."

By this time, Rachel was getting madder and madder, "Luke Koger!" she yelled, "I have to get my money back. You owe me several thousand dollars that I put into this house. If I have to, I'll sue you."

Luke got up from the bed and shouted back, "You won't have a leg to stand on! You gave me the money as a gift! Besides, your name isn't on any paper."

Rachel turned on her heel, stormed out of the house, got back in her car, and drove the ten miles to her mother's house.

Rushing into the house she yelled, "Mom! He's cheated me out of my money, and he's got another woman!"

Cora said, "I told you what a man would do when it comes to money. I never did trust him anyway."

Rachel lost her money and later retired from the military. She lives in South Carolina and continues working in a clinic with patients that have substance-abuse problems. Rachel never married. She is much like her mother. She gives all her time and energy to her work, singing, and living life to the fullest.

Cora had learned much about cruelty from her parents and about kindness from the Metcalf family. After seeing the extremes of how people could treat someone in need, Cora decided she would be kind when the opportunity to do so presented itself and not follow her parents' horrible example.

Amy Johnson

One beautiful April day in Appalachia, Cora Allen was driving her old dented green Ford to town. She saw a young teenage girl up ahead hitchhiking. Her hair was brownish blonde, she was shabbily dressed, and looked distraught.

Cora stopped the car looking at the disheveled teen and asked, "Where are you going?"

Weeping, the girl replied, "To the human resource office in town."

Cora asked, "Why do you want to go there?"

The weeping girl responded, "I'm pregnant and my mother and stepfather have thrown me out. I don't have any place to live."

Cora said, "You can live with me."

"Really? You would let me live with you?"

"Yes," Cora answered, "but your mother and father will have to sign a consent form. What is your name and where do you live?"

"My name is Amy Johnson. I live about two miles up Possum Holler. Are you kidding? Would you really let me live with you for sure?"

"Yes, provided they sign the paper, and you aren't on drugs or have a venereal disease." Cora replied.

Amy answered, "I've never taken drugs and I don't have any disease."

"Alright, I'll turn this old bucket of bolts around and head to your house right now."

"Oh, please don't do that. I'm ashamed of where I live." Amy lamented.

"It don't matter to me. I've seen all kinds of messy places in my life." Cora said.

When they got to Amy's dark and dirty shack of a house, Cora saw about a hundred chickens running loose. There was chicken manure all over the yard and front porch. The stepfather and Amy's brother were sitting on a dilapidated couch and drinking beer while watching TV. Amy's mother was wearing a faded dirty dress and looked haggard.

Cora said, "Hello, I'm Cora Allen from over Bent Holler way. I found Amy out on the West Fork Highway thumbing. She said you all kicked her out because she's pregnant. I'm willing to give her a home if you'll sign a consent form for me to take her."

The step father laughed and jeered, "You'll be sorry; she ain't no good."

Cora retorted, "I'm willing to give her a chance to prove herself. Everybody deserves a chance to do better."

The mother spoke up and said, "I'll sign. I can't keep her here with a baby. We don't have any money since I married him."

She pointed to her husband and continued, "Before I married him, we were getting a big check from Social Security from the young'uns' dead pappy. So now all the money we can rake and scrape goes to buy beer. You can give her a better home than we can. Amy, bring me a piece of paper and Cora you write it out all legal and all."

After the paper was signed, Amy and Cora went on the human resources center to sign Amy up for SSI and food stamps. Then, they went to the health department where she endured the tests necessary to prove that she was drug free and didn't have any disease. The final information would be forthcoming in a few days. They also went to a local doctor to make sure Amy's pregnancy was as it should be at her stage of motherhood. The doctor told Cora that Amy was doing well for her age and being pregnant.

Amy was dressed only in a man's faded T-shirt and a pair of jeans with a shoestring holding the jeans together at her waist because her belly was too big for the jeans to fasten normally. She also wore a pair of holey sneakers, but no socks or underwear. Cora took Amy shopping for some maternity clothes and material to make some more. She bought Amy shoes, socks, and underwear to take home with them back to Cora's house.

"How did you happen to get pregnant, Amy?" Cora asked.

"I went home with a girlfriend to spend the night and that night her brother forced me."

When they arrived at Cora's house she showed Amy which bedroom would be hers and the baby's when it was born. The room was painted pale green with tropical floral curtains and a mint green chenille bedspread.

Amy gasped, "Is this all for me? It's beautiful! Why are you doing this for me? I'm pregnant and fifteen; I don't deserve all this." She waved her arms back and forth indicating the whole room.

Cora said, "You need help. I've been in need in my life and other people helped me. You'll have to help me with housework and growing the garden and canning this summer. If you don't know how to do these things, I will teach you. It's things you'll need to know to raise your baby and someday have your own home."

Amy gave Cora a hug. "Thank you Cora; I'll help all I can. I don't know much about garden growing and canning though."

Cora said, "I'll show you. It's hard work but you'll be proud when you see all the canned fruits and vegetables we'll put up for the winter."

Cora took Amy back to the doctor each month for her checkup. The baby was growing and healthy. Spring turned into summer, and the women developed a close relationship. Cora took Amy to her church which was a one room white wood building with wooden benches. Amy enjoyed going to church. She hadn't gone to church with her parents when she was young.

They worked hard each day, but in the evening they sat on the porch swing and sang. Cora played a guitar and they harmonized by singing hymns and mountain ballads. That summer, they canned many jars of summer vegetables and fruits. They stood back and admired all their handiwork.

Amy said, "I'm sure glad you picked me up that day. I don't know what I'd have done if you hadn't."

"You're welcome. You've done very well and learned a lot about housekeeping and canning. You've been a real blessing to me, too."

One of Cora's cousins, who was retired from the military and was drawing Social Security and VA checks, was willing to sign papers saying that he was the father of Amy's baby. He didn't even know her before she came to Cora's house. It would be several months before she would get the checks, but Amy was getting welfare checks so she was able to buy clothing for herself and baby things, along with household items. Amy's belly grew and grew all summer into early fall. One night Cora noticed Amy was using the bathroom several times.

Cora asked, "Are you alright?"

Amy answered, "I'm really hurting and I'm spotting on the toilet paper."

Cora said, "You're going into labor. Get your things, we've got to get to the hospital in town."

Upon arrival, the doctor checked Amy and affirmed that she had started labor. He recommended that she stay there until the contractions got closer and the delivery was over.

Amy yelled, "Cora, Cora, don't leave me! I'm only sixteen and I'm scared."

The doctors okayed for Cora to stay, but while she was with Amy she had to wear a gown and a mask.

Amy screamed, "I'm dying!"

Cora comforted her by patting her head and saying, "No, you're going to live. Amy, I can't go into the delivery room with you when it's time, even if you wanted me to."

A few hours later a beautiful seven pound, twenty inch girl was born. Amy named her Becky after one of her friends.

When they brought Becky home, Amy had already bought a crib and baby clothes, but they couldn't find any cloth diapers. All they could find were store bought diapers. Cora said, "I can't go to town every time she needs more diapers. It's too far and expensive."

Cora bought white flannel, or, as country people called it, "outing". She got enough material to make two dozen three-foot squares. After she hemmed them on the sewing machine, they had wonderful soft diapers for Becky.

Cora said, "When she uses them, quickly rinse them out with cold water and hang them on the clothesline to dry. The cold rinse keeps them from staining. After several of them are used, bring them in and wash them in the washing machine to get 'em clean." In warm weather, Amy hung them back on the clothesline to dry again. In rainy or wintery conditions, she used Cora's clothes dryer.

Eight months after Amy applied for Social Security and VA benefits, Cora brought the mail into the house one morning.

Cora said, "Tell me what you would do with $8,000."

Amy laughed, "Oh yeah, I would buy me a car and rent me and Becky our own house."

Cora answered, "Well, get ready, because here it is! They paid you a thousand dollars a month for the past eight months."

Amy jumped up and down with glee and hugged Cora, "Oh boy! Oh boy! You'll have to help me get the things we need."

Cora said with a wide grin, "Get the baby and meet me at the car. There's no time like the present." They drove to town; Amy opened a new bank account, and deposited the check.

Cora said, "I'll show you how to write checks. Be careful with your checkbook and bank book. If someone gets them, they can get your money. Because someone could steal your purse, don't keep much money in it. Write checks for what you need. "

They drove for several miles looking for houses to rent. The first one they found was too large and would be too expensive to rent and heat. The second house was in another county. It was small and looked well cared for and it was next door to the owners. When they went the next morning to inquire about renting the property, the owners had a lease for her to sign. It stated that only Amy and Becky could live there. They could have visitors but no homesteaders. There would be no drinking or drug use in it.

Cora said, "Amy, do you promise to abide by the rules? If you break them then you will have to move."

Amy said, "I promise. I don't want people drinking or drugging around Becky, and I sure don't want any folks moving in with me either."

After signing the lease Cora, Amy, and Becky went to a used furniture store and bought two-bedroom suites with beds, mattresses, chests of drawers and bedside tables. They also got a used sofa, stuffed chairs and some side tables. Amy wrote a check to pay for them.

They went to an appliance store where they found a repossessed washer and dryer. They looked like new but came at a large discount. Then Cora spotted an electric range that had a dent in it, too.

She said, "Amy, looky here. I think this one will be a good buy for you. You need a stove and I don't think you could get one any cheaper."

After paying for the appliances, they made arrangements to have everything delivered the next day. They went back to Cora's house and ate supper. After supper they sat on the front porch in the swing and sang before bedtime.

The next day they went to Amy's new house and cleaned it before the delivery trucks arrived with the new furniture. They arranged everything to suit Amy. Amy exclaimed, "It's like a dream of the best Christmas that anyone ever had."

"It's really real. You are a good girl, Amy. I'm going to miss you when you move out here for good. It's about time you had good things happen to you," Cora answered.

Amy said, "I owe so much to you. You have been like a mother and taught me so much."

The following day, they moved all of Amy and Becky's clothes to the house. Amy had been buying linens and other household items out of her welfare checks. She used these items to finish furnishing her house. They also moved some of the canned goods that she'd helped can.

Cora took Amy and Becky to the store and bought groceries and other items they needed. Since there weren't any lightbulbs in any of the sockets, they had to buy several of them. Cora went home that night by herself and left Amy and Becky alone in their own house. It was a lonely night for both of the women.

A few days later, Cora went back to visit them.

"You need to buy a car and learn to drive. I'll teach you." Cora said.

Amy answered, "Yes, I need one really bad. "

They went to town and bought a good used car. Amy was a fast learner and soon she had her license.

Amy commented to Cora one day, "The people around here aren't friendly. I can be outside, and if they drive or walk by nobody speaks to me."

Cora answered, "They don't know you yet. I'll come over early Sunday morning and take you all to that church we passed up the road."

Everyone welcomed them at church that Sunday. Baby Becky got scared and cried when the congregation sang and shouted during the worship service.

Cora said, "Take her outside until everyone sits down for the preaching, then bring her back in. Soon she'll get used to it all and you can keep her inside."

As time went on, Becky got used to the noise of the worship service. Amy really liked the people and they accepted her into the community as one of them.

At Christmas, the church brought Amy a turkey, baskets of fruit, nuts, and tins of candy. She, Cora, and Becky had a great time eating all of the gifts. Amy brought a Christmas card for her family to Cora's house for her to mail to them. She didn't want them to know her address or come visit her.

Baby Becky grew and grew, and before long she was in school. The bus came by her door. She was very smart and developed into a good student. Amy went back to school and got her G.E.D. She also took several secretarial courses and soon got a job doing clerical work in one of the local schools.

Amy met a young man and dated him for several years, but she told Cora, "I won't marry him until Becky is out on her own."

Becky graduated her high school with honors, and was admitted to the prestigious Berea College. Cora, Amy and Becky remained very close emotionally. They have visited each other and helped each other in various ways as needs arose.

The Strangers

Do you have time for one more story? Despite all the horror they face, the generosity of good mountain people still compels them to open their homes and their hearts to those in need. I'll leave you with this mysterious example of that very generosity in action.

Charlotte White lived in Appalachia. One day she walked three miles up a holler to visit her mother, Ada Stewart. Because one of her daughters couldn't take care of the children, Ada was raising two of her granddaughters: eight-year-old Paige, and nine-year-old Paula. Ada drew a check from welfare to help with expenses like food and clothing.

Ada and Charlotte cooked a big dinner consisting of soup beans (pintos) with a slab of hog-side meat, lard-fried potatoes, mustard greens, molasses, butter, and cornbread. The family enjoyed heaping helpings of the food, washed down with cold milk. After dinner Charlotte scraped any uneaten food from each plate, and fed the scraps to their dog Tige. Next she washed the dishes, rinsed, and dried them before she put them away in the corner pie safe for storage. Then she took a crisp white tablecloth and covered the bowls on the table to keep flies out of their leftover food. The family would eat these leftovers for supper that evening.

Just then there was a knock on the door. When Charlotte opened the door, she saw a shabbily dressed old man and woman standing there carrying white feed-sack bags that were filled and tied with string.

Charlotte said, "Howdy, what do you want?"

The old man answered, "We're travelers, and we are so hungry that we are about to starve. My wife might faint any time. Could you please give us something to eat?"

Charlotte replied, "We just got finished eating, but we have some leftover grub that we could give you. Come on in."

Ada heard the conversation and came to the door. She said, "By all means, come in. Sit over there at the table and we'll warm up the food for you."

The lady served the strangers generous helpings of all the warmed food and gave them milk and coffee to drink. The strangers kept saying "Thank you! Thank you!" over and over many times as they wolfed down their repast.

After the meal, Charlotte walked them to the door and they all stepped outside. Paige called to her and she went back in the house a minute to see what Paige wanted. When she went back outside the strangers were gone. She could see about a hundred feet both ways up and down the highway, and they weren't to be seen anywhere. Charlotte walked up the road to the next door neighbor's house. The neighbor Bruce was sitting on the front porch.

Charlotte asked, "Did you see an old couple come by here or go down the road?"

The neighbor answered, "I've been sitting out here for about two hours, and I haven't seen nary a soul or a car go by here."

Charlotte related the story to Bruce, but a look of disbelief came over his face. She told the story to many people, but none of them believed her. Despite this, Charlotte and Ada rest easy in the knowledge of what really happened. Could Charlotte and Ada have been entertaining angels unaware? It's a great mystery that neither of them can explain.

Made in the USA
Middletown, DE
27 June 2022